UNBREAK MY SOUL:

How Black Women Can Begin To Heal From Workplace Trauma

BY

Dr. Carey Yazeed

Shero Books
Subsidiary of Shero Productions, LLC
Louisiana

THIS WORKBOOK WAS
Inspired by

Chichi Agorom

Dr. Elijah Anderson

Dr. Joy DeGruy

Lelah Delia

EJR David

bell hooks

Dr. Tiffany Jenkins

Toni Morrison

Sophia Nelson

Linda Tuhiwai Smith

Dr. Beverly Daniel Tatum

Dr. Charles W. Mills

INTRODUCTION

I always get asked, or more so presented with the audacity statement, "Why is your focus mainly on Black women? Why do you exclude white women? We all have the same problems." And I usually respond with a heavy sigh as I think about the many societal traumas I have endured simply because I was born Black.

Whenever someone refers to race as a 'social construct' or comments that 'the only race is the human race', I reflect on the wisdom of Toni Morrison. She wrote, "the function of freedom is to free somebody else." Although I wholeheartedly agree with Morrison, as I grow older and continue to evolve, I am constantly reminded of three things- everyone doesn't want to be free, some people don't realize they are not free, and those that keep us captive (unknowingly or knowingly) refuse to learn anything about freedom and choose instead to focus on what-about-ism. Then there are those who want to be free, but don't know how.

I think women from all walks of life can fall into any of the scenarios I've listed above, but my focus is on the latter- those who want to be free, but don't know how - specifically, Black women. Why? Because I am a Black woman! Unlike other racial groups, our lack of freedom and the lack of knowledge we have in how to acquire liberation has been passed down through many generations. Yes, our constant struggle to become liberated is unlike anything women of other cultures have ever experienced. Our freedom was stolen, our dignity and identities stripped away, and our ancestors enslaved for hundreds of years around the world. Laws and policies eventually granted our ancestors their physical freedom, but many of them remained in mental captivity. Why? Because the same governments that freed them, put underhanded systems in place to legally continue a system of oppression that impacted not only our ancestors, but their descendants - you and I - and these are the systems which keep us in bondage to this day.

"Why do we continue to turn to the oppressor to heal the impact of an oppression that they caused?"

When we talk about inequality as it relates to Black women, the conversation is often limited to discussions of unequal pay and the lack of financial resources. Has anyone stopped and considered that inequality also extends to the healing of Black women? As a former mental health therapist, I can attest that the theories taught in counseling programs center the ideologies of dead white men from the fields of sociology and psychology. These men did not consider the healing of Black people in their research studies. In fact, systemic racism and oppression continue to be prevalent, most notably in what is defined as the white savior complex.

Savala Nolan, author of Don't Let It Get You Down: Essays on Race, Gender, and the Body, and the director of the Thelton E. Henderson Center for Social Justice at UC Berkeley School of Law, explains that the white savior complex consists of a system of ideas and ideals that are rooted in superiority. The belief is that minorities are helpless, misguided and ignorant, and don't know what is best for them. Individuals who suffer from this complex believe that the only way this person or group of people will survive is if they (an entitled white person in a position of authority or superiority) comes in and saves them and/or their community (minorities) because the white savior knows what is best.

The biased training and superior attitude are not just individual issues. Consider also the licensing exams being administered for mental health therapists are white-centered and perpetuate the white savior complex. In order to pass, for a few hours test takers have to identify the therapist as a savior to pass the exam. How does this occur in professions that should not discriminate? The tests, just like the textbooks, are being developed by white clinicians who continue to center white comfort instead of developing cultural humility through collaboration and consultation with clinicians from marginalized communities.

Minority professionals are failing these exams in large numbers because their experience of helping their communities is not in alignment with predominant white thought. Another concern that I have about the testing required for licensure is the usage of algorithms to automatically flag and fail Black test takers resulting in fewer licensed Black clinicians. This shortage of knowledgeable Black mental health therapists has forced Black women to seek out help from privileged white clinicians who can not relate to us.

This underrepresentation extends into the self-help publishing industry, which has been oversaturated with rich, white suburban housewives. If we are to believe them, we'd all be walking around thinking their Disney life is attainable for everyone if we just work hard and have a positive mindset - think Brene Brown, Rachel Hollis, Jenna Kutcher and Amy Porterfield.

"Why is it so rare to find books on Black healing authored by Black scholars and clinicians?"

Because systemic racism also exists in the publishing industry with million dollar book deals being offered to the privileged white women I just mentioned, and society as a whole being fed the message that they are our saviors. Women like bell hooks die doing the same work, but are lesser known due to lackluster support from their publishers and society in general. The lack of resources available for Black women to heal is not coincidental; it is very intentional, and keeps us running to the works of these women and men whose bondage (yes, I'll admit they have issues too) is very different from ours. Their definitions of trauma and white-washed ideologies of freedom, liberty and healing, unfortunately, aren't aligned with our Black lives.

I created this workbook because I identified a problem that no one is willing to publicly address. After publishing two anthologies that focused on the impact of toxic workplaces in the lives of Black women and conducting qualitative research within the tech industry that focused on minority women trapped in corporate purgatory (between the invisible glass step and glass ceiling), I realized many of us are emotionally imprisoned. Our careers are stagnant due to fear, hurt, pain and unresolved trauma that we've pushed to the side in an effort to maintain careers, families, and a social life while juggling the constant state of our uncomfortableness within society.

Every morning, Black women suit up in their protective emotional armor in preparation to dodge the barrage of negative assumptions the day will inevitably bring. Who will I be labeled today - the angry Black woman, the aggressive Black woman, the problematic Black woman? Swinging our feet from beneath the comfort and safety of our bedding, we emotionally begin to prepare to deal with the coworker who doesn't think we are smart enough, despite having two degrees.

We hype ourselves up with coffee, energy drinks, and positive affirmations that remind us we are smart, beautiful, and important despite the underhanded comments Karen and Susan will surely direct our way throughout the day. The 'strong Black woman' will check her reflection in the mirror, practice both her smile and her responses to the many microaggressions she will endure- reminding herself not to look mean or uninterested.

She must pretend she isn't emotionally drained from dealing with the biases and ignorant encounters we endure between the hours of 9am through 5pm, Monday through Friday. Exiting her vehicle for the workday, she straightens her professional attire, checks her armor once more and then heads into the emotional battlefield that is the office.

Bathroom breaks and smoke breaks are used to call a girlfriend for moral support that consists of reminders why she needs this job and to find just one good reason why she shouldn't cuss Becky out this time. Every Black woman in Corporate America has been this woman.

We may receive a call from our husband, son, father, brother, or uncle informing us they were stopped by the police. Our heart begins to race, our chest gets tight. This feeling is familiar and it will pass as soon as we know they are okay - no, alive! We scroll through social media to help take our mind off of our toxic workspace, but see that everyone is talking about another unarmed Black man who was killed. Deep sigh. We check our bank account. Maybe some retail therapy will help. The balance staring back at us is a gentle reminder that we don't get paid enough for the hell we endure day in and day out at our job.

We practice all of the breathing techniques that we've read about from white self-help gurus, but quickly become frustrated because none of it is working. We contemplate taking off our emotional armor, 'leaning in' to our real feelings, and sharing our concerns with our work bestie, but remember that Amanda will not understand. The few times we've tried to open up, the look of confusion on her face was enough to make us stop dead in our tracks and change the subject to something lighter that she could actually relate to. We also know that if we allow ourselves to think about all of our anger, the hurt and pain will gush out and be misinterpreted. We would lose our job and be escorted off the premises by the police because we made a white person uncomfortable. Instead of seeing us leaning in, they would claim they were attacked and felt threatened by our presence and 'unpredictable' behavior.

Somehow, despite all of these challenges, we mentally make it through the work day. Returning to the comfort and safety of our home, we find ourselves unable to relax; tossing and turning throughout the night as we try to process what we've gone through and how to better protect ourselves the next day.

OVER TIME, THIS TOXIC, NEVER ENDING, EMOTIONAL CYCLE BECOMES THE NORM, JUST ANOTHER DAY IN THE LIFE OF A BLACK WOMAN IN CORPORATE AMERICA.

For Black women, both our traumas and coping mechanisms are generational-passed down from our mothers, grandmothers, aunts and cousins. From the moment we become functioning members of society, Black women, begin to live a 24/7 hypervigilant life. Unlike white women, we are rarely given a chance to rest, heal, grow and thrive because our lived experiences are filled with both the historical trauma passed down from our ancestors and the ongoing trauma witnessed in violent videos and news stories. Social media feeds and our local news cycles are filled with reports of how another Black man or woman was killed by the police or targeted by a white supremist. When you couple this with the racial and emotional trauma we experience in the workplace, it is no wonder that we remain in a neverending state of fight, flight or freeze.

Through this workbook, I want to change our narrative of healing. I want us to realize that we don't have to continue to live in an emotional state of turmoil. We can heal! And it doesn't have to be at the hands of old white men and privileged suburban white women.

Although society has set us up to live in a constant state of oppression and mental gymnastics, I'm here to share that you have an option. You can choose to pause the madness, change the narrative and write a different outcome that isn't white-washed. Take a moment to stop and reflect on how you have learned to function in trauma. Don't you want to try something different? Being a Black woman is hard. I know that because that is the only woman I've ever been. I can't speak to the experiences of white women or even Brown women because I am not them.

I am not a person of color.
I am a Black woman.
Black, Blackity, Black, Black.

I speak of what I know, which is my lived experience as a Black woman, and that is what this workbook is based on.

If you are reading this, it means your mind is tired of going through these mental obstacle courses- especially at work. It means you are ready to do what needs to be done to begin the healing process and reclaim a part of yourself; the part you've forgotten about over the years because it is hidden beneath so many layers of protective emotional amour.

I am no longer a mental health therapist and this workbook should not be taken as mental health advice. Instead, this project is written from my perspectives as a researcher, a cultural critic with a background in mental health, and a Black woman who has become an expert in navigating crazy coworkers and toxic workspaces. It is my hope that you will use this workbook to help to acknowledge your suffering and begin your journey to liberation and healing.

Dr. Carey Yazeed

UNDERSTANDING
Trauma

A Black woman's exposure to trauma begins the minute we are conceived and continues until the day we stop breathing. Many of us suffer from the impact of some type of trauma and don't realize it - especially if the trauma happened in our childhood or has been passed through multiple generations. You also may not identify some experiences that have occurred in your life or career as traumatic because they occurred over time, which desensitized you.

Some of us are living in a constant state of fight, flight or freeze - our body's involuntary reaction to a perceived threat- which impacts how we respond when faced with certain situations. This is trauma.

According to the American Psychological Association, trauma is defined as an emotional response to a horrible event like war, a car accident, rape, or surviving a natural disaster. Immediately after the event, shock and denial typically occur. The long term effects of trauma include erratic and unpredictable emotions, flashbacks, strained relationships, shaking, headaches, ringing in the ears and nausea.

Trauma is divided into three specific categories; acute, chronic and complex.

- Acute Trauma occurs from a single episode/exposure to a harmful event. We normally associate this type of trauma to someone witnessing a person being killed.

- Chronic Trauma is present when a person is exposed to repeated and prolonged harmful incidents. This type of trauma is congruent with an individual who grows up in a home where domestic violence occurs.

- Complex Trauma happens through varied and multiple traumatic events that are often invasive and interpersonal in nature. This type of trauma is commonly seen in indigenous people who have been exposed to various levels of systemic racism.

The diagnosis that is commonly associated with trauma and is recognized by the American Psychological Association and is billable for mental health therapy is **Post Traumatic Stress Disorder (PTSD)**. PTSD is a diagnosis assigned to individuals who have experienced or witnessed a traumatic event. Symptoms of PTSD can include nightmares or unwanted memories of the traumatic event, avoidance of situations that remind one of the trauma, heightened reactions, anxiety or depression.

Other diagnostic labels not recognized by the American Psychological Association, but are just as significant in the fight for the healing of Black women and further explain why we begin to cover ourselves with protective armor include- **Historical Trauma, Post Traumatic Slave Syndrome** and **Post Tramatic Relationship Disorder.** The research of Dr. Maria Yellow Horse Brave Heart indicates that Historical Trauma (also known as Intergenerational Trauma) is caused by prior events that targeted a certain group of individuals, but ultimately impacts generations of their family members.

Similarly, according to Dr. Joy DeGruy (2005) Post Traumatic Slave Syndrome exists because Blacks were subjected to multigenerational trauma (slavery) and experienced oppression and institutionalized racism over a prolonged period of time. **Post Traumatic Relationship Disorder** (Matthew J. Friedman, 1995) is a condition that occurs when we allow dysfunction and trauma from past intimate relationships to influence our behavior in current intimate relationships.

This falls more in line with domestic abuse between intimate partners, a parent suddenly leaving the home and eliminating all communication and physical contact with a child, or infidelity. None of these conditions are listed in the Diagnostic and Statistical Manual of Mental Disorders (DSM), a publication by the American Psychiatric Association that is used to classify mental disorders. However, they are significant criterias to use when trying to understand the emotional distress that Blacks -especially Black women- experience.

I first realized that I had Post Traumatic Stress Disorder after being sexually harassed while working as a college professor. While preparing to teach a class one evening, a male graduate student trapped me in my office, while alone in a building on campus. After the incident, my symptoms included crying on my way to work each day, my hands would shake uncontrollably, and I would have panic attacks anytime I heard a bell ring, (The perpetrator would wait for me to get off of the elevator each day I arrived at work.

The bell in the elevator sent a signal to my brain that the trauma was about to start.). Long term, I isolated myself. I physically stopped interacting with people and left the physical workspace in 2016, only accepting remote work and engaging with clients via Zoom. Going outside became a chore and often intensified my anxiety. If someone was coming to visit or a package was being delivered, I timed it so I could open the door before they rang the doorbell. These coping mechanisms became my protective armor.

I remember people close to me not understanding, telling me I was overreacting and needed to get over it. This was pre-COVID, before the rest of the world realized they also suffered with mental health issues caused from workplace trauma too. Instead of allowing them to influence how I chose to protect myself, I avoided them and I stopped talking about my experience. When people asked why I left higher education I simply told them it no longer suited me.

TYPES OF WORK
Trauma

When we think about trauma, we normally picture domestic abuse, veterans returning from war, survivors of mass shootings, or sexual assuault victims. Seldom does our place of employment or our profession immediately come to mind. Society has conditioned us to not consider how capitalism can be traumatic or how trauma can be experienced in the place where we dedicate the majority of our time - work! In addition to the trauma from our interpersonal experiences with racism, and those that have been passed down from previous generations, we often encounter gender bias, microaggressions, ageism, ableism, discrimination and harassment in professional spaces.

Ableism is discrimination in favor of able-bodied individuals. The two main types of ableism are physical and mental ableism. Physical ableism is hate or discrimination against a person because of their physical limitations and or appearance. Mental ableism is the hate or discrimination against a person based on their mental health condition and cognitive difference. Ableism can show up in recruitment when job descriptions mandate all employees be able to lift 50lbs for a position that could in fact be done by someone in a wheelchair, or when a person with autism isn't granted reasonable accommodations that will help them to perform their job well.

Gender Bias is when a person is treated differently because of their gender identity. Gender bias against cisgendered women is sometimes related to maternity. In some instances, women have not been hired or promoted because she either hasn't started a family or it is assumed she wants to start a family and her productivity will slow down once she gets married and begins to have children. Gender bias also appears as likeability. If a woman speaks up, she is perceived as being aggressive and if she says nothing, she is seen as weak and easily intimidated.

Microaggressions are how biases show up in the workplace. Microaggressions can be related to any number of things and are hostile, derogatory, and subtle. Black women have been told for years that braids and afros are unprofessional yet more Eurocentric styles are the epitome of workplace propriety. Women of color also encounter surprise at their intelligence and are 'complimented' on how well they speak- especially if they are not originally from America. These 'compliments' are condescending instead of praise and are meant to highlight differences.

Discrimination is when a person's rights are infringed upon due to their race, age, disability, or gender identity. An example of discrimination is an organization not promoting the qualified Black woman with a solid and diverse 20-year record with the company in favor of a white male with less experience and education from the outside.

Sexual Harassment involves the use of explicit or implicit sexual overtones, unwelcomed or inappropriate promises or rewards in exchange for sexual favors. A manager bullying an individual contributor to have sex with them, touching them inappropriately, or making unwanted sexual advances and then threatening to fire the subordinate worker if they tell anyone is a form of sexual harassment.

Gaslighting is when someone psychologically manipulates another person into questioning their own sanity or tries to control them by twisting their sense of reality. An example of gaslighting in the workplace would be a manager or coworker belittling your efforts or perception, saying negative things about your work performance to others but within your hearing range, or not inviting you to meetings that are relevant for you to effectively do your job.

According to an article by Sandy Smith for Enhanced Health Today, other types of workplace trauma may include:

- Layoff/Job Loss
- Workplace Violence
- Death of a Colleague
- Natural Disaster that Impacts Your Workplace
- Unequal Pay/Pay Gap

When we talk about toxic work environments and workplace trauma as Black women, we rarely (if ever) discuss the Black woman leader who devalues the Black women under her leadership. This is a chronic problem. Our silence usually stems from the generational warnings of Black families, "what happens in our house, stays in our house!" But, why can't we talk about and begin to understand the trauma we sometimes cause each other in the workplace?

There are several reasons why Black women in leadership roles make life a living hell for the Black women who work with them. In order for a Black woman to make it into leadership, she had to learn how to mimic the behaviors of her white male counterparts. Instead of being warm, engaging and understanding, she was most likely coached to change her behavior to be colder, less approachable, and neutral. As a result, she became stern and condescending, making you feel less than the woman you really are.

Some Black women in leadership positions experience intense feelings of intimidation and fear of failure. Imposter syndrome fools some of these women into believing that they must protect their position before the next Black woman comes along and takes it. They feel it is necessary to keep their foot on your neck at all times to remind you that your place in Corporate America is beneath them.

There is also the perception that other Black women are not good enough. This concept stems from slavery-era thinking that although Blacks are inferior to whites, Blacks in the fields were inferior to Blacks who worked in the "big house". Some Black women in leadership stop identifying with us and instead align themselves with the people who have a seat at the table - which isn't you and I. She begins to compare your education, work history and even your private life to her own. She believes she is better than you because the proverbial door was opened and the sacred seat granted to her, not you.

"Hurt people, hurt other people."

Many Black women in leadership have been hurt, and instead of seeing a therapist, they wear trauma like a badge of honor. These women honestly believe that before the next Black woman 'makes it', she has to experience hurt too. We know that at some point in her career she experienced bullying, microaggressions, harassment, racism and unconscious biases.

Before the summer of 2020 - when a world health crisis and the live stream of a Black man being killed in broad daylight by the police made everyone realize Black people were traumatized - she kept those corporate hurts to herself. Unfortunately, they began to fester like a sore and then run.

Yes she is special. She is the chosen one, and we can never take that away from her. BUT! As the Black woman on the receiving end of her abuse, please remember this; her objective isn't to reach back and help the next Black woman to climb the corporate ladder. No, once she made it to the promised land she slammed the door in our faces and then deadbolted it.

So what should you do if you find yourself in this type of abusive relationship with your supervisor? In the words of Carolina Wanga, former Chief Culture, Diversity & Inclusion Officer for Target and now CEO of Essence Communications,

"If you can not be who you are where you are,
you change where you are, not who you are."

PROTECTIVE
Gear

Earlier, I mentioned emotional armor and described how we put on layers of protection after we experience a trauma. As we experience new workplace trauma, we add additional layers to our emotional protective gear. Your Monday work personality is not the same as the person you are on the weekends. When you walk out of your door every weekday morning or turn on your computer to begin your virtual work day, you unconsciously put on all of your emotional armor. Unfortunately, it has become such a habit that you no longer consciously think about. But, in the depths of your mind, heart and soul, every trauma you have ever experienced in life, including in the workplace, is still there. You've done an exceptional job of masking the hurt over the years.

I have encountered women who wear so many layers of emotional armor that when I ask about workplace trauma they immediately deny ever experiencing an unpleasant work culture. They claim that they have never been on the receiving end of bias, microaggressions, discrimination or sexual harassment. I'm not one to argue, but if they are a woman of color, especially a Black woman, that is highly unlikely. She has probably forced herself to block out those incidents so that she can push forward. She never addressed the trauma. Instead, she reached into her war closet and pulled out a nice, pretty piece of armor to further protect herself. Over the years, she has likely become desensitized to the negative comments, actions and even her own feelings. She has convinced herself that no one will believe her, because "I am the only woman going through this ish anyway!"

These are some common emotions/symptoms experienced by victims of workplace trauma, which may cause Black women to reach for their armor:
- Feeling Numb
- Trouble Sleeping
- Trouble Concentrating
- Inability to Maintain a Regular Routine
- Feeling Constant Pressure to Overwork
- Digestive Issues
- Anxiety, Panic Attacks, Anxious
- Depression
- Relationship Issues Such as Withdrawal From Family and Friends
- Outbursts of Anger or Aggression

You must allow yourself time to process your emotions and heal. If you do not, the symptoms you are experiencing will only get worse as time goes on. You may lose focus of your professional goals, but continue to show up everyday, not realizing that you are not the same person you were earlier in your career.

As you can see, trauma isn't one dimensional neither is self-care and healing. You have also learned that marginalized groups, including Blacks, have survived specific traumatic events and the aftermath continues to impact the current generation. Now that you have a better understanding of what trauma is, let's move through several exercises that will help you to identify your trauma and begin the healing process.

There is just so much hurt, disappointment, and oppression one can take...

The line between *reason* and *madness* grows *thinner*.

ROSA PARKS

My first "official" job was working at a retail store called Fashion Gal, which was located in a popular mall where I lived. A church member was the manager and when I applied for a job, she hired me as a sales associate. I was only paid minimum wage, but I didn't care. I was a sixteen year old girl who read Seventeen Magazine like it was the Holy Bible. Now I had money to buy the trendy fashions I often read about and I was around fashion and fashionable people all day! This was a dream come true for a fresh-eyed teen who prided herself on keeping up with the latest fashion styles and trends.

I loved working there. I dreaded the fact that the position was only for the summer, and I would have to resign once high school resumed that fall. I was approaching my senior year and my parents would not allow me to work during the school year. My plans were to take advantage of the discounts and use this opportunity to fund my summer and fall wardrobe, but I gained so much more during the few months that I worked there.

This experience turned out to be more than fast fashion for a teenage girl. Instead, it became the foundation of who Dr. Carey Yazeed is, and how she felt inside when she went to work each day. I learned that I liked helping people to look and feel their best and showing them how to embrace their assets. I also learned what it felt like to be in a family environment and love what you do- you know, where people actually look out for you. I began to understand the importance of knowing that your boss and customers appreciate you and what you do for them. I also confirmed that I loved fashion, thinking outside of the box, and standing out in a crowd. I was only seventeen, but this was a life changing experience I would find myself searching for thirty years later.

Unfortunately, I would not have another job experience like this one until I worked as a Social Work Instructor and Director of Field Education in the Department of Social Work at Southern University A&M College. This was also the first time in my professional life where I wasn't micromanaged and was allowed to freely do my job. Not only did enrollment increase in the department once I began teaching (and recruiting students in the elevator to become social work majors), but I was able to reach students where they were. I was skilled at identifying when they were struggling and offering assistance so they wouldn't fail. I watched with pride as individuals who were ready to give up, walked across the stage as the first in their family to obtain a college degree. That experience was just as life changing as my job at Fashion Gal. The last time I had this feeling of awareness as a professional was when I embraced full time entrepreneurship in 2016.

So, what was the point in my sharing this story with you? Before we became aware of racism, oppression, bias, discrimination and harassment in the workplace, we were somewhat naive, innocent beings. Slowly the protection of our parents, our nuclear family unit, and our communities, began to subside and we were introduced to a world that no longer embraced us, protected us, or loved us. If you are reading this you may be feeling desperate, alone, disgusted, and hopeless, but you are still determined as hell to not let this be your final narrative!

Using the space below, I want you to think about a time in your professional career when you didn't know what hurt was in the workplace. I want you to close your eyes and sit for a while; reflect on your innocent career moments: the time(s) in your life when you were unaware of discrimination, uneqaual pay, microaggressions, and gender bias. What did this moment in time mean to you? How did you feel while working during this innocent period in your life? Remember the smells, the sounds, the voices, and how those around you made you feel. What made this time special for you? Describe the professional you during this time period.

_____

_____

_____

_____

_____

_____

_____

_____

_____

_____

This is who you are at your core as a professional Black woman. When you peel back the layers of emotional protective armor that you've developed over the years to protect you from the ugliness of the workplace, this is who you are. The goal over the years has been to protect and keep her safe. Unfortunately, in the process you forgot who this version of you was.

Now that you remember her, your goal is to liberate her!

Innocence is one of the most exciting things in the *world*.

EARTHA KITT

In hospital settings, code red is an emergency code used by staff to indicate fire, smoke or smell of smoke. Code Red indicates danger. Often in our professional careers, there is a code red, but instead of us realizing the signaling is an indicator that we are in danger and that our professional lives are on fire, we view the warning as if it's a bad hair day and try to use hair mist to put out a raging fire.

My first code red experience with workplace trauma occurred during my first professional job as a social worker. I had taken a position in the adolescent unit at a psychiatric hospital. The sparks started to show in my interview. The line of questioning should have warned me it was a toxic work environment, but back then I didn't know what was considered appropriate interview questions nor the definition of a 'red flag.' The interviewer, who was a white woman a few years my senior, wanted to know how I could afford to attend Tulane University, a private school located in New Orleans, Louisiana. She shared that she had to attend Louisiana State University to obtain the exact same master degree that I had due to their inexpensive tuition. She went on to tell me that she didn't think it was fair that I had the opportunity to obtain a better education than her (her words, not mine) and wanted to know how I was accepted and again, how my family could afford the tuition.

I'll admit, I was somewhat naive and her question went over my head. I remember being puzzled that she was asking me about how I obtained a degree instead of my experience and qualifications for the position. I had been to several job interviews and no one had asked me this. But then again, all of my interviews had been with other Tulane alumni. So I was honest with her;

"I applied and was accepted. I was offered work study as a form of tuition assistance and had to take out student loans to cover the balance plus my housing. My parents didn't assist with my tuition or cost of living because my younger brother was in college at Southern University. They had helped me financially while I completed my undergraduate studies, but they could not afford to help both of us and I had to figure it out myself."

Naively, I also went on to tell her that she probably would have been accepted if she took the initiative to apply, and could have afforded to attend if she signed her life away with student loans too!

Ironically, she hired me.

Two weeks later, she hired my white counterpart, a female who had less experience than me and had graduated from Auburn University, but was a native of Louisiana. I was assigned the task of 'training' her. We were both young, but I noticed her quality of life appeared to be better than mine. She had a brand new, fully loaded Honda Accord, and she attended graduate school without having to take out any student loans. She wore designer clothes everyday and she smelled expensive! She came from a prominent white Southern family.

They didn't approve of her career choice, but appeared to calm down when she told them how much she was making at the hospital. I remember my eyebrows went up slightly and there was this sunken feeling in the pit of my stomach. So I asked, *"How much are they paying you to work here?"* I remember her salary being $10K more than what I was making.

Now remember; we had the same degree, both had attended private schools, but I had more experience than she did due to internships in both undergraduate and graduate school which focused on adolescent mental health. She went on to share with me that after her 'training' period she was going to be moved into the supervisory position for the adolescent unit. Mind you, there was a Black woman who had been working in the unit for years and technically she should have been promoted into the role over all of us!

My mouth flew open and the hot tears formed in the corner of my eyes. She asked what was wrong. I told her nothing and then excused myself from our office. I immediately went to speak with our supervisor - the one who couldn't understand how I could afford to attend Tulane University. I walked into her office and asked about the pay difference. She smiled and told me that it was unprofessional to discuss salaries, that it was her duty to look out for her white counterpart, and maybe I needed to contact the good Jewish people who let me into Tulane and see if they would give me a higher paying job. Then, she told me to get back to work.

The words, "I quit," tumbled out of my mouth. I didn't think about what I was saying, the words just came out. She told me I couldn't quit because the adolescent psych unit would be short handed. I told her it was a great day for her to learn what really took place and why she probably should have paid me that extra $10K.

I remember as I walked out, my hands were shaking. I had begun to sweat as I thought to myself, "What in the hell just happened?!" and "Isn't there some type of employment law that governs equal pay?"

Then I began to think, "Now what?"

Then I began to panic, "Girl, you don't have a job!"

I'd moved back in with my parents after graduate school because I couldn't afford to live on my own with the salary I was making. As I entered my parents home, they stared at me and asked why I had returned so early. I told them what had happened. Oddly, they didn't look surprised or shocked and told me I could help out with our family catering business until I found another job.

No one explained to me that this was my first encounter with workplace trauma or that during that incident I had begun to develop my first layer of emotional armor to protect me in the workplace. More importantly, no one warned me that as I began to move throughout my career each new traumatic workplace experience would add a new layer to my armor and that eventually, it would begin to weigh me down.

Many experiences of workplace trauma followed over the years. I have dealt with white social workers who projected their white savior complex onto me and clients of color, believing I couldn't possibly be as smart as them. I was never good enough and in their eyes, I didn't know what my clients needed. They believed I couldn't possibly be as smart as them and for years, I endured unequal pay and I believed the hype that if I got another certification or another degree, I would be seen as equal and compensated appropriately for my knowledge and experience. Throughout my twenty-six years in the field of social work, I encountered microaggressions, unconscious bias, blatant racism and discrimination from many elite white women in the field - yes a profession where workers are suppose to show empathy and compassion.

I soon realized social services was really a place where suburban white women retreated when they became bored being stay at home housewives, and desired to do more than just ruin the school's PTA.

Thinking back, my first experience with personal trauma came at a much earlier age. This layer was formed after my mother spanked me because I fell asleep with gum in my mouth. When she woke me, the gum was all over my expensive lace stockings. I remember the anger when she realized I had ruined them. The look in her eyes scared me for the first time in my life. It was the look she gave my dad when their arguing would escalate into throwing objects and name calling.

As a result of that spanking, I spent my entire childhood working overtime emotionally to avoid upsetting her (or anyone else). I was already an introverted child, but after that incident, my goal was not to be seen nor heard and to never be the cause of anyone's anger again. The protective gear that I selected was silence.

Throughout the years, other protective layers developed as a result of participating in desegregation in public schools. I lived in the last school district in America (Baton Rouge, Louisiana) that refused to abide by the Brown vs. The Topeka Kansas Board of Education Supreme Court ruling, and the federal government had to step in. As a result, I was bused across town to an all white school where I had to quickly learn how to navigate aggression, biases and racism as a child.

My parents didn't talk to me about hate and people not liking me because of the color of my skin. I wasn't told about inequalities and how my classmates came from generational wealth. No one explained that I shouldn't take the negative statements that my white teachers and classmates said about me seriously. The protective layer that I developed to shield me from the hurt associated with segregation was perfectionism.

I had to dress perfect, my hair had to be perfect, and my school work had to be perfect. I could never give anyone a reason to say anything negative about me. In the summer of my freshman year at college, I developed another protective layer after my dad beat me so badly I was unrecognizable for weeks. He was drunk and thought I was talking back to my mom. As a result, I added the layer of not expressing myself and hiding my true feelings. After having to fight off two young men who tried to rape me in college, the additional layers of trusting no one and never placing my self in a physical setting to be taken advantage of were added. Can you imagine how heavy my armor had become?

Throughout my life, I fortified my armor with layers I developed to deal with colorism within my own family. I watched my mother and some of my aunts show favoritism towards my cousins who had lighter complexions than I. I layered on being a people pleaser and overachiever so that my family members' eyes would sparkle for me the same way they did for those with less melanated skin.

Countless layers were added to deal with the systemic racism of having the police pull me over and tell me to go back to my side of town because I was a Black teenager driving in a white neighborhood. Layer, after layer, after layer was added after watching crack cocaine take over my urban neighborhood and people I grew up with become the living dead. My armor became even heavier after viewing the killing of Black people at the hands of the police on the news day in and day out. I developed layers to protect me from an emotionally abusive ex-husband, his refusal to co-parent and being labeled by society as an angry Black mother while trying to protect my two Black sons from the dangers of racism in the South.

Never did I stop to realize that all of this trauma and armor had started to weigh me down. After being sexually harassed on a job, having my co-workers (more social workers) consciously make me relive the trauma daily, and the experience I was enduring with the perpetrator, I emotionally hit rock bottom. I started to cave under the heaviness and I just wanted to escape from it all. I had become suicidal. The weight of my armor had become too much to bear.

It wasn't until 2021 that I sat down and began to search for the young girl who didn't fade into silence. I had to find the person who loved her job as a sales associate at Fashion Gal. I desperately needed to find these versions of myself and figure out what happened.

I yearned to have that innocence back and the lightness of not having the weight of all the emotional armor I had been carrying. I wanted to return to that teenager who saw the workplace (and the world) through a fresh lens each and every day. I needed to find the little girl who chewed gum without fear of being hit by her mother. I wanted to laugh from my belly, smile with all of my teeth, and be ignorant to the fact that America could be an evil place that hated women - especially women with skin like me. I needed to find her and then liberate her from the years of emotional bondage, workplace trauma and societal trauma that she had endured, but first I had to remember who she was.

As I stated earlier, with each new trauma in my life, another protective layer was added to shield my soul from the emotional hurt and psychological pain. Those layers consisted of being an overachiever, a people pleaser, and a human shield. My armor consisted of not trusting anyone and cutting people off before they had a chance to hurt me. It included smiling and making sure I never let anyone around me see the pain that I was going through; to always look the part of the agreeable Black woman vs the angry Black woman. My armor included a white box that went with me to every new job and could hold all of my personal items if I needed to leave quietly, but suddenly.

You see, we use various emotional armors to protect the person we were before we experienced any type of hurt or trauma - your inner self. You are now aware that trauma doesn't have to be drastic like gun violence or domestic violence. It can be as simple as feeling your emotions shift from positive to negative for the first time and how you pivoted to protect your innocent, younger self.

Now I want you to take a moment and think back to your younger self. When did you put on your first layer of armor to protect her? Describe the incident. How did you feel? What was the armor that you selected? Why did you select that particular emotional armor? How long did you wear the armor or are you still wearing it?

_____

_____

_____

_____

_____

_____

_____

_____

_____

_____

_____

_____

_____

_____

_____

_____

_____

_____

Next, I want you to think about the personal trauma you have faced in your life as a Black woman. This can include systemic racism, poverty, physical and/or emotional abuse, sexual assault, your parents divorcing, you getting a divorce, ended friendships, etc. Again, what happened? How did it make you feel? What emotional layer of armor did you grab to protect yourself?

_____

_____

_____

_____

_____

_____

_____

_____

_____

_____

_____

_____

_____

_____

_____

Finally, think about the trauma you have experienced in the workplace - discrimination, inequality, low pay, microaggressions, bias, sexual harassment, etc. What were the specific incidents? Who was involved? How did these toxic situations make you feel? What emotional layer of armor did you pick up to protect yourself?

_____

_____

_____

_____

_____

_____

_____

_____

_____

_____

_____

_____

_____

_____

_____

_____

Emotionally this can feel like a heavy moment for you. It's okay to step away, breathe, ground yourself by going outside and walking barefoot on grass or just sitting in the sun and soaking up the rays. You may feel a heaviness that requires you to process how you are feeling and that is okay.

This is how the healing process starts.

You may not *control* all the events that happen to you, but you can *decide* not to be reduced by them.

MAYA ANGELOU

In this next exercise, I want you to reflect on the times in your career when you have experienced trauma in the workplace. It doesn't have to be your current place of employment. Think back to former jobs. Have you ever felt uncomfortable, noticed a change in your behaviors - think about what was the root of you feeling this way and write it down below.

_____

_____

_____

_____

_____

_____

_____

_____

_____

_____

_____

_____

_____

_____

_____

_____

_____

_____

_____

_____

_____

_____

_____

_____

_____

_____

_____

_____

_____

Now might be a good time to check in with your mental health therapist. If you don't have one, begin to seek out the services of a professional that can help you if you are starting to feel uneasy/uncomfortable with these exercises. A great place to start is Therapy for Black Girls or Psychology Today which are online directories of therapists that provide mental health services.

We must reject not only the stereotypes that others hold of us, but also the stereotypes *that we hold of ourselves.*

SHIRLEY CHISOLM

I want you to stop and allow yourself to think about your past jobs, the past hurts you've listed. Now think about how you've coped. How did you continue to show up every day? What layer(s) of emotional protective gear did you put on before you walked out of your door every morning? Using the space below, write about those experiences and the emotional layers of protective armor you wore to work each and every day to shield you from toxic people or attitudes.

_____

_____

_____

_____

_____

_____

_____

_____

_____

_____

_____

_____

_____

_____

What I know for
sure is that
speaking your truth
is the most powerful
tool we all have.

OPRAH WINFREY

Check in

In the first half of this workbook you removed the scabs from some old wounds that may not have healed properly over the years. You may be feeling raw and very emotional. Take a few moments to gather your thoughts, listen to your breathing - inhale, exhale. Now, using the space below write how you are feeling about the exercises you've completed. How are you feeling about yourself and what does all of this - the uncovering of workplace trauma, your hurts and pains now mean to you? Ask yourself, have you truly healed or did you bury it under layers of emotional protective armor, hoping it would go away? How many layers of armor are you wearing? Be honest.

PART TWO
JOURNEY TO
Healing
AND LIBERATION

JOURNEY TO
Healing & Liberation

You've unpacked a lot in the last few pages of this workbook. This was done on purpose so that you would understand what workplace trauma is and rediscover the person you used to be before you layered on the armor and started protecting your former professional self.

In the second half of this workbook, the focus will be on healing and liberation.

Despite what the white self-help gurus have told you, healing from workplace trauma looks differently for Black women because of an additional layer of trauma that has resulted from years of systemic oppression. As discussed in Part One of this workbook, Black people experience what I call the trauma of being Black in society; having to navigate living while being a Black person and all of the trauma that is associated with our varied experiences that have taken place outside of the workplace.

In her book, The Enneagram for Black Liberation, Chichi Agorom reminds us that Blacks live with their vulnerabilities being exposed daily. She cautions that it isn't healthy for us to 'lean in' because that will only further place us in danger. Instead, we need to become aware of our vulnerabilities, our trauma, and our protective armor and then begin to consciously make the choice to put certain pieces of armor on and also to remove it when we are in safe spaces.

How do we begin to heal? Well, you've already started. The first step was to identify your workplace trauma, which I am sure also has you thinking about the other forms of systemic oppression you have encountered. The next step was to understand how you protect yourself and identify the different layers of protective emotional armor that you wear daily. Now, you are going to give yourself grace. You are going to discover what it feels like when you don't wear your armor- the vulnerable you.

We often blame ourselves for the trauma we have endured, especially in our professional careers. When we are at home alone, maybe with a candle lit and a glass of wine, we tend to pick ourselves apart. We unconsciously talk negatively to ourselves for not reaching certain career goals, however, we must realize that we have actually checked all of the boxes! Our lack of progress has nothing to do with us and everything to do with them, their biases and systemic racism.

So where does your liberation come in? This is a good question. The freedom for Black women in society and the workplace will come from three things:

1. Knowing what your vulnerabilities are in society and the workplace.

2. Understanding that your armor doesn't define who you are. It is not your identity. Like clothing, it is something that you wear. It is emotional protective gear that you should reach for to help shield your vulnerabilities from the dangers you face.

3. Learning that you have a choice when it comes to removing your armor and that it isn't necessary to wear it 24/7.

4. Realizing that you have to listen to your body. Learn how to create a sense of interpersonal safety from within because the world outside of your body is not going to provide the safety that you need.

5. Identifying which layers of your armor are no longer needed and which ones you can temporarily put aside.

In the first half of this book, we have covered points one and two - knowing what your vulnerabilities are and understanding that your armor doesn't define who you are. You now have a better grasp of what has gone wrong and why those layers of armor were needed. Hopefully, you're more aware that the need for emotional armor has not been your fault. In this section, you are going to give yourself grace, discover that it is okay to be vulnerable, and identify when it is okay to remove your armor. You will learn how to listen to your body and begin to create your own safe spaces that will allow you to be emotionally naked.

LETTER TO
Yourself

Using the space below, I want you to write a letter to the professional you were before you experienced your first workplace trauma. Let her know how life has turned out, what some of the obstacles have been, how you have protected her throughout the years and how you are going to liberate her - to free her. Even if you don't have a plan, let her know that you are going to try. Describe the resources you will use - career coach, mental health therapist, start your own business, find a new job, get a promotion, move to a new team at work, contact the Equal Employment Opportunity Commission (EEOC), speak with an employment lawyer - reassure her that protection is going to start looking different and it will no longer involve hiding. Give her grace, acknowledge her, comfort her, reassure her everything is going to be okay.

_____

_____

_____

_____

_____

_____

_____

_____

_____

_____

When you take care of yourself, you're a better person for others.

When you feel good about yourself, you *treat others better*.

SOLANGE KNOWLES

IT TAKES A VILLAGE
to Heal

There is an old African proverb, "It takes a village to raise a child." I also believe it takes a village to heal. Unfortunately, many Black women are scared to reach out for help or don't know who they should turn to. Worse yet, they struggle to identify someone who will believe them so instead of risking another blow to their soul, they remain silent and suffer alone.

I recently read a review for an anthology I presented which focused on the toxic experiences of Black women in the workplace. The reviewer stated,

"I honestly felt that these were the same stories over and over again...some of the stories were exaggerated and hard to believe...there should have been a diverse background of characters or job positions in order to make the stories more relatable."

I shook my head in frustration. The stories of Black women and their experiences are too often negated or downplayed with comments like, "That couldn't have possibly happened to you." "That seems kind of far fetched." " Stop exaggerating," I know because I heard these exact same words when I sought out help for my own workplace trauma. This is a major reason why many Black women never share what they have gone through. They choose instead to suffer in silence because they fear no one will believe them. There is also a belief that the traumatic experiences of Black women are all going to be unique. Unfortunately the same scenarios are playing out in Corporate America daily. The names may change, but the victims are always Black women. Unfortunately, we (Black Women) don't realize we are all having the same horrific experiences in the workplace because we don't talk about them. And, let's not forget that many will negate the experiences of others because they haven't dealt with their own trauma and pain. It's easier to either dismiss the negative experience of someone else or have others question their validity than to publicly admit you have the same exact issues. It is much more difficult to admit that you have become desensitized and suppressed your experience to prevent having to deal with the aftermath of it again.

While growing up, many of us were told, "What happens in this house, stays in this house!" Unfortunately, this has stuck with us and keeps us afraid to seek out support. We were never encouraged to share our emotions, downfalls and traumas with others. Instead, we were taught to deal with them in solitude. As we ventured into adulthood, some of us carried this mantra with us. Black women continue to refute therapy, choosing to "take everything to the Lord in prayer", trying to hold it all together alone, and never discussing their hurts, pains, trauma, discomfort and losses. And then, in 2020, the global pandemic forced us all inside and people found themselves sitting with their issues, unable to escape or avoid them.

During this time, we saw a significant increase in Black women (and men) utilizing their mental health benefits. Many discovered that the anxiety and depression they had attributed to the pandemic were, in reality, manifestations of deeply rooted trauma that had been covered with protective armor for years.

During this time, we also witnessed the consistent rise of unemployment rates and a mass exodus that would come to be known as the 'Great Resignation'. Working from home helped many Black Women realize their work environments were toxic. Because there were no microaggressions, racism, discrimination and harassment to deal with, they felt more relaxed and were able to accomplish more in a short period of time. For the first time, many were able to complete their work without being burdened by the heaviness of their emotional protective armor. When employers and the government started to force everyone back into buildings, some resisted. Many Black women sought new jobs that allowed them to avoid the traumatic and unsafe conditions and continue their healing.

Despite these advantages, working in isolation can limit the kinds of support available to you. If this is your situation, you will have to tap into your current village of family and friends. In some cases, you may need to go out and find a village that will support you and provide the safe space, tools and resources that you will need as you continue to find your way to happiness and inner peace. So, what should a support village look like for a Black woman who is removing her protective armor?

Your village should consist of others who understand what you have gone through/ are currently going through, and they will hold space for you to talk and release your pent up emotions without passing judgment. Your village may also include a mental health therapist who specializes in the kind of trauma you've encountered. A solid village could also include a weekly support group where strangers with similar issues come together to talk, learn and grow with the understanding that the secrets shared within that sacred space never leave. A nurturing village may include a mentor or career coach that guides you through your journey of transitioning into a new role/ position. Village members are people who will be there for you, understand you, uplift you and guide you. They are the support you need so you can safely begin to remove the emotional protective gear that you've been wearing, rediscover the beautiful soul that has been hidden and finally release her into the world.

Using the space below, make a list of individuals, groups and resources that are (or can be) your village. These individuals are able to hold space for you as you begin to safely peel back the layers hidden beneath your protective armor. It's time to release your soul, release your mind, release that beautiful person who you've been protecting all these years from the ills of society.

PEOPLE WHO UNDERSTAND YOU

MENTAL HEALTH SUPPORT

SUPPORT GROUP

MENTOR/COACH

Remember, it's important to meet with members of your village on a regular basis, not just when you are hurting or need to vent. They should also be included in the wins, joys and celebrations of your life. How often will you meet with your villagers? Will your meetings be consistent - same day, same time, once a week, every other week or monthly? Remember, consistency will remind your brain that you have an outlet and decrease your emotional need to fight, flee or freeze.

SELF LOVE IS
the Best Love

Self-care is self-love and both are intricate parts of every healing process, no matter the hurt or pain you are trying to overcome. Learning to love yourself means learning how to listen to your body. It is identifying when you are hurting, finding the source of your pain (which you've already done), and providing yourself with the nurturing that you need to be emotionally and physically healthy. Self-care and self-love mean understanding what makes you smile and feel alive. You have been in unsafe spaces for so long that your body has been in a constant state of fight, flight, freeze and you've needed to suit up to protect yourself. Self-care and self-love is identifying how you feel when you are in a safe space where it is okay to remove your armor.

Many of us are walking around shell shocked. We've been hurt by society and our war with systemic racism never stopped, hence the healing we should have been doing never happened. Unfortunately, we have become accustomed to the emptiness and pain, and we think it is just a part of who we are, just like our protective armor. When we don't learn to love ourselves, the hurt never goes away. Instead it festers like a sore and begins to run - showing up as the angry Black woman, the bitter Black woman, and the problematic Black woman. When we don't heal, we lash out and hurt others. Remember - hurt people, hurt people.

Once you understand what it takes to love your inner self, you'll begin to thrive in life and in your career. There will be a positive shift in your demeanor. You will feel more in control of your feelings and your reaction to certain situations. Self-love will allow you to quickly identify when there is a code red in your professional life; however instead of reaching for hair mist to try and put it out, you'll better understand when it is okay to walk away from situations that are detrimental to your inner peace.

Sometimes it can be difficult to know where to start when it comes to nurturing and loving yourself. On the next page you'll find a thirty day chart filled with activities to help you get started. Figure out which self care activities work best for you and set aside time to begin engaging in the activities that help you to relax, recharge, and learn to love yourself again.

30 DAYS *Self Love*

DAY 1 Start the work diary in Part Three of this book	DAY 2 Take a 15 minute walk around your neighborhood	DAY 3 Take a bubble bath and light your favorite candle	DAY 4 Make your favorite meal	DAY 5 Read a book that you enjoyed as a teenager
DAY 6 Listen to your favorte song	DAY 7 Take yourself to lunch	DAY 8 Wear a cute outfit to work or to run errands	DAY 9 Go to bed 30 minutes early	DAY 10 Get a manicure in a fun color
DAY 11 Give yourself a facial	DAY 12 Create your favorite drink	DAY 13 Try a new meal and/or new restaurant	DAY 14 Watch your favorite movie	DAY 15 Unplug from social media for 24 hours
DAY 16 Give yourself a facial	DAY 17 Listen to a podcast that's easy & fun	DAY 18 Compliment yourself in the mirror	DAY 19 Watch the sunset while sitting outside	DAY 20 Schedule a massage
DAY 21 Clean out your closet. Give away clothes that no longer fit	DAY 22 Turn off your phone and computer for 24 hours	DAY 23 Lay on the floor on your back and breathe	DAY 24 Visit a park and swing on a swing set	DAY 25 Try a new hobby
DAY 26 Plant something- veg garden, house plant or a tree	DAY 27 Buy yourself some fresh flowers and place on your desk	DAY 28 Make a vision board that represents goals you'd like to accomplish	DAY 29 Write inspirational quotes on sticky notes and place where you can see them daily	DAY 30 Start the work diary in Part Three of this book

TELL ME
Something Good

As you begin to remove the layers of protection, you must add a light gauze to your wounds to help them continue to heal. Instead of using layers that keep you from being your genuine, authentic self, I want you to cover and protect yourself with positive words of affirmation. Each morning, before you begin your work day, look in the mirror and repeat these affirmations. There's space below where you can add additional words of affirmation.

"I am a gift!"

"I am reaching outside of my comfort zone to make my dreams a reality."

"I am in control of my life."

"I am not going to let my environment control me. I am going to control my environment."

"I am successful."

"I am a warrior, I've got this!"

"I am more powerful than I think!"

"My mind only has space for positive thoughts."

"I am stronger than my current situation."

"I am a beautiful person both inside and out."

"No weapon formed against me shall prosper."

"I am fabulous!"

"I have brilliant ideas."

"I am building my own table."

Use the space below to write your own positive affirmations

_____

_____

_____

_____

_____

_____

_____

_____

_____

_____

_____

_____

_____

_____

_____

_____

SETTING HEALTHY
Boundaries

Having healthy boundaries is beneficial for every professional - including you. Healthy boundaries help you identify when to remove your armor or replace it. They also help you to avoid job burnout, develop your identity as a professional, ensure you have good emotional health and help you to find more fulfillment in your career. This helps you to have a less stressful professional life.

Healthy boundaries also help to develop your autonomy. When setting boundaries, you learn how to make decisions based on what is best for you instead of what is best for others. A lack of boundaries not only opens the door for emotional manipulation from others in your life, but you also waste a lot of time catering to the needs of others which can become stressful.

SIGNS OF UNHEALTHY BOUNDARIES INCLUDE:

- You share too much about yourself to coworkers
- You close yourself off and don't ask for help
- You feel responsible for the happiness of your boss and/or co-workers
- You are unable to tell boss and/or co-workers no
- You base how you feel about yourself on how your supervisor and/or co-workers treat you
- You allow your co-workers to make decisions for you
- You feel powerless at work
- You don't take responsibility and/or initiative for your own career. You are waiting on someone else to point you in the right direction

When it comes to setting boundaries, the first step is recognizing how you feel when your boundaries are violated. Do you feel angry, guilty, or fearful? Do you resent the person? Once you understand how the lack of boundaries impacts your emotions, it becomes easier to start establishing them. Here are the next steps you should take when setting boundaries in the workplace:

1. Identify what boundary is needed and with whom

2. Communicate the boundary to the individual(s)

3. Keep your explanation simple - maybe write it down so you don't get off course

4. State what the consequences will be if this boundary is crossed

To help you get started, here are a few examples of how to set professional boundaries:

- Set a designated time to check work emails (i.e once in the morning, after lunch and one hour before it's time to clock out for the day)

- Stop accepting work calls once you've clocked out for the day

- Become comfortable telling co-workers and your supervisor, "no"

- Do not follow your coworkers on social media and don't allow them to follow you (Block them!)

- Speak up when you feel violated in the workplace

- Communicate any discomfort you feel in your workspace

- Do not accept blame when a co-worker or boss is trying to displace a problem onto you

- Use your PTO. You do not owe anyone an explanation for taking time off - it's your time, use it

- Know that it is okay to change your mind - just because you said yes to a project yesterday doesn't mean that you can't reconsider. If it no longer fits your goals, it's okay to change your mind

- Take responsibility for your career. Develop a professional plan each year that includes action steps and track your progress monthly

- Keep your private life and your professional life separate

- Engage in activities that allow you to develop your individual identity

NAME THEM

Inside of the heart, identify who you need to set boundaries with at work and why.

BOUNDARY

Activity

We all have that one coworker we know that we need to set some healthy boundaries with, but struggle to do so. Using the activity sheet below, let's work on setting a healthy boundary with that specific co-worker.

1. Who do you need to set a healthy boundary with at work?

_____

_____

_____

_____

2. Why do you need to set a healthy boundary with this coworker?

_____

_____

_____

_____

3. How does this person make you feel when they violate your boundaries?

_____

_____

_____

_____

4. What is the specific boundary that you need to put in place with this person?

_____

_____

_____

_____

_____

_____

5. How will you communicate this new boundary to this person?
Remember to keep your explanation simple.

_____

_____

_____

_____

_____

_____

6. What will the consequence be if this boundary is violated?
Remember to convey this to them as well.

_____

_____

_____

_____

_____

_____

GIVING THANKS
Showing Gratitude

Part of healing involves acknowledging the significant people and things in your life and giving thanks. In addition to reflecting on what has gone wrong, each day it is imperative that you remind yourself of the positive outcomes, people and experiences that are woven throughout your life. Take a moment to shine a daily spotlight on what has gone right.

Focusing on the positives and showing gratitude causes a shift to take place within our soul. We move from a place of negativity to one of enlightenment and positive thinking. It helps us to see the bright side of our situations and, more importantly, gives us hope - especially when we are starting to feel down and hopeless.

It is easy to become fixated on what is going wrong and to wallow in self pity. This can be another piece of armor that you wear to protect yourself from workplace trauma. Using the work diary in Part Three of this workbook, at the end of each day you will write down three things that you are grateful for and/or three people who made a positive impact on your life and why.

In addition to utilizing the work diary, here are a few activities to help you start giving thanks and showing gratitude at work.

- Greet your coworkers in the morning (it doesn't matter if they speak to you or not)
- Surprise a coworker who has been helpful by buying them lunch or gifting them with a $10 gift card to their favorite coffee shop
- Give your co-workers compliments when you notice something positive about them or when they've done a great job on a project/presentation
- Say thank you often when a co-worker helps you or offers assistance
- Recognize effort from your team members - even when a project goes wrong
- Purchase a blank card and write a helpful co-worker a thank you note
- Be sincere when saying congratulations, offering condolences, or giving well wishes
- When a coworker is out sick, send them a get well care package

GRATITUDE *Activity*

Let's get in the habit of being grateful. Using the space below, answer each question as it pertains to you today. Afterwards, reflect on what you are grateful for and how it makes you feel when you are able to identify the people and things in your life that you appreciate.

List three things that happened today that you are grateful for:

1. _____
2. _____
3. _____

List three people that you are grateful for today and why:

Person #1 _____
Why are you grateful for them?
_____

How did you show your gratitude?
_____

Person #2 _____
Why are you grateful for them?
_____

How did you show your gratitude?
_____

Person #3 _____
Why are you grateful for them?
_____

How did you show your gratitude?
_____

TAPPING INTO YOUR
Spirituality

We all believe in something that is greater than us. Be it God, Allah, Yahwah, Jehovah, the ancestors, crystals, or metaphysics, throughout our lifetime we have learned to develop some type of relationship with that greater entity. But, we do not always tap into it. As you learn to love yourself from a deeper perspective, I believe it is equally important to reconnect and strengthen your relationship with that Higher Being.

As I was going through my nervous breakdown, I was not in a good mental space. I could not explain to a human being outside of my therapist what I was going through. During this time, I found reconnecting with God and my ancestors to be very valuable. I made time to meditate, pray, read my Bible and sometimes just be still and do absolutely nothing other than taking in the sounds of nature and observing the world around me.

Please do not solely focus on this part of the book and neglect everything else. Our spirituality is a significant key to healing, but it isn't the only piece of this intricate puzzle. You will need to engage in other activities as well.

But, back to spirituality. Tapping into a higher calling helps us to find our centeredness and rediscover the purpose for why we are here. Connecting with something greater than us can provide a source of strength, calmness and solitude.

Using the space below, describe how you will begin to connect with the entity which you believe is the creator of all things. How much time will you devote to this part of your life? How will you use that time (prayer, meditation, reading, praise, simple conversations)?

_____

_____

_____

_____

_____

_____

_____

_____

_____

_____

_____

_____

_____

_____

_____

_____

_____

GROUNDING Yourself

We've discussed how trauma can have symptoms like anxiety and depression, or trigger fight, flight or freeze feelings within us. Trauma can show up in the form of nightmares, or panic attacks triggered in the middle of a work event. These are moments where you may feel helpless, hopeless and afraid. When you begin to experience these symptoms, you may feel as if you have lost touch with reality and become trapped in your hurt and pain (even if it is brief). You may also find yourself lost in the memories that are centered around your trauma.

Grounding exercises help you to emotionally return to the here and now - the present. They can be quick exercises like taking a few deep breaths or longer exercises such as going outside and walking on grass barefoot. Everyone's experiences are different and the grounding exercises that bring you back to reality may not work for others.

There are some examples of grounding exercises listed below. Try a few until you find the ones that work best for you. Just like all trauma is different, we all will use different exercises to return to reality. You may even find yourself using different techniques for different symptoms/reactions.

GROUNDING *techniques*

The Australian organization, Living Well offers several grounding techniques you can try when you feel disconnected, when your emotions shift, when you begin to experience a panic attack, or when you are triggered. They include:

- Remind yourself of who you are now. Say your name. Say your age now. Say where you are now. Say what you have done today. Say what you will do next.

> *"My name is Jane, and I am 54 years old. I am in my living room, in my home, on Gentilly Avenue, in New Orleans, in Louisiana. I woke up early today. I had a shower and fed my dog. I just finished my coffee and toast. Soon I am going to get in my car and go to work. I am going to drive down P aris Avenue and then turn right by St. Leo the Great Church. Then I am going to...."*

- Take ten slow breaths. Focus your attention fully on each breath, on the way in and on the way out. Say the number of the breath to yourself as you exhale.

- Splash some water on your face. Notice how it feels. Notice how the towel feels as you dry your skin. Use words in your mind to describe the sensation.

- Sip a cool drink of water.

- Hold a cold can or bottle of your favorite soft drink in your hands. Feel the coldness, and the wetness on the outside. Note the bubbles and taste as you drink it.

- If you wake during the night, remind yourself who you are and where you are. What year is it, what age are you now? Look around the room and notice familiar objects and name them. Feel the bed you are lying on, the warmth or coolness of the air, and notice any sounds you hear.

- Turn your attention to the clothes on your body, whether your arms and legs are covered or not, and the sensation of your clothes as you move in them. Notice how your feet feel to be encased in shoes or socks, or resting on the floor.

- If you are with other people, and you feel comfortable with them, concentrate closely on what they are saying and doing, and remind yourself why you are with them.

- If you are sitting, feel the chair under you and the weight of your body and legs pressing down onto it. Notice the pressure of the chair, or floor, or table against your body and limbs.

- If you are lying down, feel the contact between your head, your body and your legs, as they touch the surface you are lying on. Starting from your head, notice how each part of your body feels, all the way down to your feet, on the soft or hard surface.

- Stop and listen. Notice and name what sounds you can hear nearby. Start with the closest or loudest sounds. Gradually move your awareness of sounds outward, so you are focusing on what you can hear in the distance.

- Hold a mug of tea in both hands and feel its warmth. Inhale its scent. Don't rush drinking it; take small sips, and take your time tasting each mouthful.

- Look around you, notice what is in front of you and to each side. Name and notice the qualities of large objects and then smaller ones.

- Pick one interesting object in your field of vision. Trace its outline with your eyes, as if you were drawing its lines.

- Get up and walk around. Take your time to notice each step as you take one, then another.

- Stomp your feet, and notice the sensation and sound as you connect with the ground.

- Clap and rub your hands together. Hear the noise and feel the sensation in your hands and arms.

- Wear an elastic band on your wrist (not tight) and flick it gently, so that you feel it spring back.

- If you can, step outside, notice the temperature of the air and how it is different or similar to where you have just come from.

- Stretch.

- Notice five things you can see, five things you can hear, and five things you can feel, taste, or smell.

- If you have a pet, spend some time with them. Notice what is special and different about them.

- Run your hands over something with an interesting texture. Describe it in your mind, as if you have never felt anything like it before.

- Get an almond, or some seeds. Focus on how it looks, feels and smells. Put it in your mouth and roll it around, noticing the textures. Chew it slowly and mindfully, before noticing how it feels to swallow.

- Put on a piece of instrumental music. Give it all of your attention.

- Another option with music is to sit with a piece of paper and a pen. Start drawing a line as the music plays, representing it in the abstract on the page. Follow the music with the pen.

- If you have a garden or some plants, tend to them for a bit. Plants, and actual soil, can be an excellent "grounder!"

If you are finding that your current workplace culture isn't helping in your healing, it may be time for a change of scenery. Yes, that means it's time for you to develop an exit plan. When developing a strategy to leave your job, you need to take several things into consideration:

- How can your current employer prepare you for the next phase of your life? Do they pay for continuing education and certifications that you may need to move forward and advance your career? How long will you need to remain at your current job if you take advantage of these perks?

- If you are planning to start your own business, I highly advise that you put away at least six months of savings to live off of in case of an emergency. What does that look like for your financial situation?

- Use your current job to finance your next move. Use your salary to buy inventory for your new business, to hire a career coach, to have your resume revised.

- Check into your benefits, including unused leave time. Will you be reimbursed for unused leave, if not, how much paid time can you take off that will not appear alarming to your immediate supervisor? Does your employer offer COBRA for health benefits once you resign? How will you cover health insurance if it is not offered at your new place of employment or as an entrepreneur?

- Begin to network. If you are planning to move to a new company or start your own business, you need to get out of your comfort zone, start meeting new people and networking. Attend professional events that will allow you to meet new people, toot your own horn. Let people know what you do and what you would like to do in the future.

- Speaking is a great way to gain attention. Volunteer to present at conferences and events within your profession. This puts you in front of your target audience and/or next employer.

- Clean up your LinkedIn profile. Depending on which industry you are in, recruiters turn to LinkedIn to scout new talent. Does your headliner showcase your skills and tell what you do and what problem you solve? Do you have a professional headshot (not a car selfie). Do you have a professional banner? Have you highlighted presentations, books you've written, podcasts you've been a guest on? Is all of your relevant work experience listed? Have you identified the hiring managers at companies you are interested in working at and requested to connect?

EXIT Strategy

Using the space below, map out your exit strategy. How long can you remain at your current job? During that time, what are some things you can do right now to make you employable at a new company? If your goal isn't to return to Corporate America but instead to start your own business, what steps do you need to take to transition into entrepreneurship either part time or full time?

_____

_____

_____

_____

Where do you see yourself as a professional in three months?

_____

_____

_____

_____

Where do you see yourself as a professional in six months?

_____

_____

_____

_____

Where do you see yourself as a professional in nine months?

_____

_____

_____

_____

Where do you see yourself as a professional a year from now?

_____

_____

_____

_____

Actions Steps - What are the steps you need to take to successfully exit your current job and move into a position that will benefit you financially, mentally, physically and professionally?

NOTE: You should work on one action step per week.

Step	Due Date	Status After 1 Month *(Not Started, In Process, Completed)*
_____	_____	_____
_____	_____	_____
_____	_____	_____
_____	_____	_____
_____	_____	_____

What is your centering word for the month:

_____

A centering word is used to help you stay focused, it is an adjective that currently describes you and your attitude as an individual.

DOCUMENTATION OF TOXIC BEHAVIORS
In the Workplace

"If there isn't any documentation, it didn't happen." When I worked as a social worker, one of the most valuable lessons I learned was documentation. Detailed reports of home visits, counseling sessions, and conversations with family members and community resources were always needed if we had to represent a family in court. I remember on one occasion, the judge only wanted to read my notes in the client's file and didn't want to hear from me. He warned me, "it had better tell me a story!" And trust me, it did

If you've found yourself in a toxic workspace, you will need documentation if you are planning to file a report with the Equal Employment Opportunity Commission (EEOC). The EEOC is a federal agency that handles discrimination cases in the workplace. If you are planning to meet with an employment or civil rights attorney for bias, harassment or dangerous work environments, they are going to want a paper trail.

In addition to printing out every email, memo and any other documentation that will help your case (YES, I said print. Some companies use software that can erase emails and their attachments on both ends with a click of the mouse) you will also need to have your own personal documentation. Instead of trying to recall incidents from memory, you need to document toxic incidents and conversations immediately after they occur.

All of your documentation needs to be kept in a secure file away from your place of employment, preferably in a locked file cabinet at your home. Yes, electronic copies are great, but as I've just explained, they can easily disappear so always have a hard copy handy.

On the next page, you will find several copies of incident reports. Again, it is imperative that you keep your own documentation regarding work related incidents that make you uncomfortable, feel like an attack, or could possibly warrant additional attention. Use these sheets to record any encounters with co-workers, customers, or leadership such as microaggressions, biases, racism, discrimination, etc. When you get to the last blank report, make copies and keep them with you in a safe place. Not only does this type of documentation help you to build a case, but writing it down helps you to release the frustration, hurt and pain so that you do not have to hold on to what happened.

PERSONAL INCIDENT
Report

DATE: _____

Time incident occurred?

Who was involved:

Why did this bother you:

What was your reaction? Was it effective?

Did anyone else witness this incident? If yes, who? What did they say? What was their reaction?

Was this a situation that needs to be reported to your supervisor, the police, EEOC, or a civil rights/employment lawyer?
YES ☐   NO ☐

Can you continue to safely work here?
YES ☐   NO ☐

If not, what is your exit plan? How will you safely transition out? What steps do you need to take?

How are you feeling - mentally I physically:

Do you need to speak to a mental health counselor or utilize the Employee Assistance Program (EAP)?   YES ☐   No ☐
(If yes, contact HR to learn about your EAP benefits I Check Your Health Insurance Regarding Mental Health Coverage)

Did you share your work day with your support system? What was their reaction?

What are some things you can do to help you feel better?

Additional Notes:

PERSONAL INCIDENT
Report

DATE: _____

Time incident occurred?

Who was involved:

Why did this bother you:

What was your reaction? Was it effective?

Did anyone else witness this incident? If yes, who? What did they say? What was their reaction?

Was this a situation that needs to be reported to your supervisor, the police, EEOC, or a civil rights/employment lawyer?
YES ☐   NO ☐

Can you continue to safely work here?
YES ☐   NO ☐

If not, what is your exit plan? How will you safely transition out? What steps do you need to take?

How are you feeling - mentally | physically:

Do you need to speak to a mental health counselor or utilize the Employee Assistance Program (EAP)?   YES ☐   No ☐
(If yes, contact HR to learn about your EAP benefits | Check Your Health Insurance Regarding Mental Health Coverage)

Did you share your work day with your support system? What was their reaction?

What are some things you can do to help you feel better?

Additional Notes:

PERSONAL INCIDENT
Report

DATE: _____

Time incident occurred?

Who was involved:

Why did this bother you:

What was your reaction? Was it effective?

Did anyone else witness this incident? If yes, who? What did they say? What was their reaction?

Was this a situation that needs to be reported to your supervisor, the police, EEOC, or a civil rights/employment lawyer?
YES ☐   NO ☐

Can you continue to safely work here?
YES ☐   NO ☐

If not, what is your exit plan? How will you safely transition out? What steps do you need to take?

How are you feeling - mentally | physically:

Do you need to speak to a mental health counselor or utilize the Employee Assistance Program (EAP)?   YES ☐   No ☐
(If yes, contact HR to learn about your EAP benefits | Check Your Health Insurance Regarding Mental Health Coverage)

Did you share your work day with your support system? What was their reaction?

What are some things you can do to help you feel better?

Additional Notes:

PART THREE
WORK
Diary

WHY YOU SHOULD DOCUMENT
Your Work Journey

Oprah Winfrey said it best, "keeping a journal will absolutely change your life in ways you've never imagined." In order to move forward, it is important that we understand our journey. As humans, we document different aspects of our lives; marriage, the birth of a child, purchasing our first home, etc…but rarely do we document our work journey.

When looking back on your career, can you honestly trace how you moved from one position to the next? Can you recall what events led to a specific promotion or the final straw that made you quit the job from hell? We spend approximately 160 hours a month at our place of employment, yet most of it is a blur. Many of us go through the work day on autopilot, unable to recall the little details of what made us smile, who irritated us and the goals we finally achieved.

This work diary is a tool to help you begin to document your work experience; the good, the bad and the ugly. The goal of this diary is to provide a constructive outlet for reflecting on your work life, setting professional goals, monitoring your professional progress, and pinpointing the difficulties and challenges that are holding you back from that promotion. Using this diary every work day for an entire month will allow you to capture snapshots of your work journey so that you can identify patterns of success (or the lack thereof), plan for the future and get inspired. Use it to document how far you have come so you can plan where to go next and navigate it all with grace.

HOW TO USE THIS
Work Diary

PROFESSIONAL GOALS

We tend to become so overwhelmed with the day to day tasks of our jobs, we put off working to fulfill our dreams. One day, usually when something drastic happens, we look up and realize we have become stagnant. It's ten years later, and we are still in the same position, working at the same job, and feeling overlooked and unaccomplished. The goal sheet allows you to set and track your professional goals, so that you can grow as a professional. Each month, a new goal sheet should be completed.

PREPARING FOR THE DAY

If you don't plan to succeed then you are planning to fail. Completing the 'preparing for the day' sheet will allow you to start each work day with a focused plan. This sheet will help you to be intentional about all aspects of your work day - including how you will network and toot your own horn - and it provides an outline for how you will work to achieve your professional goals.

MIDDAY CHECK-IN

Instead of aimlessly going through your work day, at lunchtime you should check in with yourself and take a moment to breathe and reflect. Review your 'preparing for the day' sheet. Jot down notes about how you are feeling or what obstacles have occurred during the first half of your day. Brainstorm ways to overcome those obstacles during your last few hours at work.

END OF THE WORK DAY REFLECTION

At the end of each day, before you go to bed, use this sheet to reflect on the events of the day; accomplishments, mishaps, situations that made you uncomfortable, what or who made you smile. This sheet also provides space for you to express your gratitude.

DAILY DIARY PROMPT

Prompts help you to reflect on your day and sort through conflicting thoughts. They inspire you to think differently about yourself and find hope in what may appear to be a hopeless situation. Each daily diary page has a different prompt. At the end of each work day, use the prompt to guide your writing.

END OF THE MONTH CHECK-IN

Just as you reflect on the end of each work day, it is equally important that you reflect on your accomplishments at the end of each month. Give yourself a pat on the back for your achievements. Take a look at what went wrong and how you can resolve those issues in the following month. This sheet should be completed at the end of each month.

PROFESSIONAL Goals

MONTH

Each month you should be working on a professional goal to either learn a new skill, prepare yourself for a promotion or to start a new job. Using the space below, think about your current situation. What would you like to be different? What action steps can you take this month to make that a reality in the next 30, 60, 90 days?

What changes would you like to see within your career/as a professional?

What is your centering word for the month:

A centering word is used to help you stay focused, it is an adjective that currently describes you and your attitude as an individual.

Actions Steps - You should work on one action step per week.

Step	Due Date	Status
		(Not Started, In Process, Completed)

PREPARING FOR
the Day

DATE

On a scale from 1 to 10 how are you feeling this morning:
1 is Horrible - Why do I even bother with this job and 10 is great - I love my job!

What action step will you work on today to help you reach your professional goal:

How will you toot your own horn/promote yourself today:

Who will you network with? Where do they work? Why are they relevant to your professional goal?

What or who might trigger or irritate you today?

What can you do to calm yourself if you become triggered/irritated?

Who will hold you accountable for your professional goal today?

TODAY'S
Affirmation

MID-DAY
Check-In

During your lunch break, use this space to document your thoughts and feelings or anything that has happened at work (this can be good or bad). If you need to thoroughly document a specific incident, please complete a Personal Incident Form.

END OF THE DAY
Reflection

On a scale from 1 to 10 how was your work day?
1 being horrible and 10 being perfect

What/Who made you smile today at work?

Why did this/they make you smile?

What step(s) did you accomplish toward your professional goal today?

If you didn't work on your professional goal today, what stopped you?

How did you toot your own horn/promote yourself?

Who did you network with today? How was the experience? Was it beneficial? What will you do differently tomorrow? If you didn't network today, what stopped you?

Were there any situations that made you uncomfortable, nervous, anxious, sad, angry, cautious?

If you had a good day, describe what happened:

How can you continue to have more good days at work?

As you end your day, what three things/people are you grateful for? Why?

What are you going to do this evening to relax/practice self-care?

End Of The Day Affirmation:

DAILY DIARY
Prompt

What do you need to get off your chest today?

PREPARING FOR *the Day*

DATE

On a scale from 1 to 10 how are you feeling this morning:
1 is Horrible - Why do I even bother with this job and 10 is great - I love my job!

What action step will you work on today to help you reach your professional goal:

How will you toot your own horn/promote yourself today:

Who will you network with? Where do they work? Why are they relevant to your professional goal?

What or who might trigger or irritate you today?

What can you do to calm yourself if you become triggered/irritated?

Who will hold you accountable for your professional goal today?

TODAY'S
Affirmation

MID-DAY
Check-In

During your lunch break, use this space to document your thoughts and feelings or anything that has happened at work (this can be good or bad). If you need to thoroughly document a specific incident, please complete a Personal Incident Form.

END OF THE DAY
Reflection

On a scale from 1 to 10 how was your work day?
1 being horrible and 10 being perfect

What/Who made you smile today at work?

Why did this/they make you smile?

What step(s) did you accomplish toward your professional goal today?

If you didn't work on your professional goal today, what stopped you?

How did you toot your own horn/promote yourself?

Who did you network with today? How was the experience? Was it beneficial? What will you do differently tomorrow? If you didn't network today, what stopped you?

Were there any situations that made you uncomfortable, nervous, anxious, sad, angry, cautious?

If you had a good day, describe what happened:

How can you continue to have more good days at work?

As you end your day, what three things/people are you grateful for? Why?

What are you going to do this evening to relax/practice self-care?

End Of The Day Affirmation:

DAILY DIARY
Prompt

What do you need less of in your life?

PREPARING FOR
the Day

DATE

On a scale from 1 to 10 how are you feeling this morning:
1 is Horrible - Why do I even bother with this job and 10 is great - I love my job!

What action step will you work on today to help you reach your professional goal:

How will you toot your own horn/promote yourself today:

Who will you network with? Where do they work? Why are they relevant to your professional goal?

What or who might trigger or irritate you today?

What can you do to calm yourself if you become triggered/irritated?

Who will hold you accountable for your professional goal today?

TODAY'S
Affirmation

MID-DAY
Check-In

During your lunch break, use this space to document your thoughts and feelings or anything that has happened at work (this can be good or bad). If you need to thoroughly document a specific incident, please complete a Personal Incident Form.

END OF THE DAY
Reflection

On a scale from 1 to 10 how was your work day?
1 being horrible and 10 being perfect

What/Who made you smile today at work?

Why did this/they make you smile?

What step(s) did you accomplish toward your professional goal today?

If you didn't work on your professional goal today, what stopped you?

How did you toot your own horn/promote yourself?

Who did you network with today? How was the experience? Was it beneficial? What will you do differently tomorrow? If you didn't network today, what stopped you?

Were there any situations that made you uncomfortable, nervous, anxious, sad, angry, cautious?

If you had a good day, describe what happened:

How can you continue to have more good days at work?

As you end your day, what three things/people are you grateful for? Why?

What are you going to do this evening to relax/practice self-care?

End Of The Day Affirmation:

DAILY DIARY Prompt

What qualities do you admire most about yourself?

PREPARING FOR
the Day

DATE

On a scale from 1 to 10 how are you feeling this morning:
1 is Horrible - Why do I even bother with this job and 10 is great - I love my job!

What action step will you work on today to help you reach your professional goal:

How will you toot your own horn/promote yourself today:

Who will you network with? Where do they work? Why are they relevant to your professional goal?

What or who might trigger or irritate you today?

What can you do to calm yourself if you become triggered/irritated?

Who will hold you accountable for your professional goal today?

MID-DAY
Check-In

During your lunch break, use this space to document your thoughts and feelings or anything that has happened at work (this can be good or bad). If you need to thoroughly document a specific incident, please complete a Personal Incident Form.

END OF THE DAY
Reflection

On a scale from 1 to 10 how was your work day?
1 being horrible and 10 being perfect

What/Who made you smile today at work?

Why did this/they make you smile?

What step(s) did you accomplish toward your professional goal today?

If you didn't work on your professional goal today, what stopped you?

How did you toot your own horn/promote yourself?

Who did you network with today? How was the experience? Was it beneficial? What will you do differently tomorrow? If you didn't network today, what stopped you?

Were there any situations that made you uncomfortable, nervous, anxious, sad, angry, cautious?

If you had a good day, describe what happened:

How can you continue to have more good days at work?

As you end your day, what three things/people are you grateful for? Why?

What are you going to do this evening to relax/practice self-care?

End Of The Day Affirmation:

DAILY DIARY
Prompt

What does success mean to you?

PREPARING FOR
the Day

DATE

On a scale from 1 to 10 how are you feeling this morning:
1 is Horrible - Why do I even bother with this job and 10 is great - I love my job!

What action step will you work on today to help you reach your professional goal:

How will you toot your own horn/promote yourself today:

Who will you network with? Where do they work? Why are they relevant to your professional goal?

What or who might trigger or irritate you today?

What can you do to calm yourself if you become triggered/irritated?

Who will hold you accountable for your professional goal today?

TODAY'S
Affirmation

MID-DAY
Check-In

During your lunch break, use this space to document your thoughts and feelings or anything that has happened at work (this can be good or bad). If you need to thoroughly document a specific incident, please complete a Personal Incident Form.

END OF THE DAY
Reflection

On a scale from 1 to 10 how was your work day?
1 being horrible and 10 being perfect

What/Who made you smile today at work?

Why did this/they make you smile?

What step(s) did you accomplish toward your professional goal today?

If you didn't work on your professional goal today, what stopped you?

How did you toot your own horn/promote yourself?

Who did you network with today? How was the experience? Was it beneficial? What will you do differently tomorrow? If you didn't network today, what stopped you?

Were there any situations that made you uncomfortable, nervous, anxious, sad, angry, cautious?

If you had a good day, describe what happened:

How can you continue to have more good days at work?

As you end your day, what three things/people are you grateful for? Why?

What are you going to do this evening to relax/practice self-care?

End Of The Day Affirmation:

DAILY DIARY
Prompt

What do you need more of in your life?

PREPARING FOR
the Day

DATE

On a scale from 1 to 10 how are you feeling this morning:
1 is Horrible - Why do I even bother with this job and 10 is great - I love my job!

What action step will you work on today to help you reach your professional goal:

How will you toot your own horn/promote yourself today:

Who will you network with? Where do they work? Why are they relevant to your professional goal?

What or who might trigger or irritate you today?

What can you do to calm yourself if you become triggered/irritated?

Who will hold you accountable for your professional goal today?

TODAY'S *Affirmation*

MID-DAY
Check-In

During your lunch break, use this space to document your thoughts and feelings or anything that has happened at work (this can be good or bad). If you need to thoroughly document a specific incident, please complete a Personal Incident Form.

END OF THE DAY
Reflection

On a scale from 1 to 10 how was your work day?
1 being horrible and 10 being perfect

What/Who made you smile today at work?

Why did this/they make you smile?

What step(s) did you accomplish toward your professional goal today?

If you didn't work on your professional goal today, what stopped you?

How did you toot your own horn/promote yourself?

Who did you network with today? How was the experience? Was it beneficial? What will you do differently tomorrow? If you didn't network today, what stopped you?

Were there any situations that made you uncomfortable, nervous, anxious, sad, angry, cautious?

If you had a good day, describe what happened:

How can you continue to have more good days at work?

As you end your day, what three things/people are you grateful for? Why?

What are you going to do this evening to relax/practice self-care?

End Of The Day Affirmation:

DAILY DIARY
Prompt

What do you need to get off your chest today?

PREPARING FOR
the Day

DATE

On a scale from 1 to 10 how are you feeling this morning:
1 is Horrible - Why do I even bother with this job and 10 is great - I love my job!

What action step will you work on today to help you reach your professional goal:

How will you toot your own horn/promote yourself today:

Who will you network with? Where do they work? Why are they relevant to your professional goal?

What or who might trigger or irritate you today?

What can you do to calm yourself if you become triggered/irritated?

Who will hold you accountable for your professional goal today?

TODAY'S
Affirmation

MID-DAY
Check-In

During your lunch break, use this space to document your thoughts and feelings or anything that has happened at work (this can be good or bad). If you need to thoroughly document a specific incident, please complete a Personal Incident Form.

END OF THE DAY
Reflection

On a scale from 1 to 10 how was your work day?
1 being horrible and 10 being perfect

What/Who made you smile today at work?

Why did this/they make you smile?

What step(s) did you accomplish toward your professional goal today?

If you didn't work on your professional goal today, what stopped you?

How did you toot your own horn/promote yourself?

Who did you network with today? How was the experience? Was it beneficial? What will you do differently tomorrow? If you didn't network today, what stopped you?

Were there any situations that made you uncomfortable, nervous, anxious, sad, angry, cautious?

If you had a good day, describe what happened:

How can you continue to have more good days at work?

As you end your day, what three things/people are you grateful for? Why?

What are you going to do this evening to relax/practice self-care?

End Of The Day Affirmation:

DAILY DIARY
Prompt

Describe a place or time when you felt happiest.

PREPARING FOR
the Day

DATE

On a scale from 1 to 10 how are you feeling this morning:
1 is Horrible - Why do I even bother with this job and 10 is great - I love my job!

What action step will you work on today to help you reach your professional goal:

How will you toot your own horn/promote yourself today:

Who will you network with? Where do they work? Why are they relevant to your professional goal?

What or who might trigger or irritate you today?

What can you do to calm yourself if you become triggered/irritated?

Who will hold you accountable for your professional goal today?

MID-DAY
Check-In

During your lunch break, use this space to document your thoughts and feelings or anything that has happened at work (this can be good or bad). If you need to thoroughly document a specific incident, please complete a Personal Incident Form.

END OF THE DAY
Reflection

On a scale from 1 to 10 how was your work day?
1 being horrible and 10 being perfect

What/Who made you smile today at work?

Why did this/they make you smile?

What step(s) did you accomplish toward your professional goal today?

If you didn't work on your professional goal today, what stopped you?

How did you toot your own horn/promote yourself?

Who did you network with today? How was the experience? Was it beneficial? What will you do differently tomorrow? If you didn't network today, what stopped you?

Were there any situations that made you uncomfortable, nervous, anxious, sad, angry, cautious?

If you had a good day, describe what happened:

How can you continue to have more good days at work?

As you end your day, what three things/people are you grateful for? Why?

What are you going to do this evening to relax/practice self-care?

End Of The Day Affirmation:

DAILY DIARY
Prompt

What was your greatest fear, and how did you conquer it?

PREPARING FOR
the Day

DATE

On a scale from 1 to 10 how are you feeling this morning:
1 is Horrible - Why do I even bother with this job and 10 is great - I love my job!

What action step will you work on today to help you reach your professional goal:

How will you toot your own horn/promote yourself today:

Who will you network with? Where do they work? Why are they relevant to your professional goal?

What or who might trigger or irritate you today?

What can you do to calm yourself if you become triggered/irritated?

Who will hold you accountable for your professional goal today?

TODAY'S
Affirmation

MID-DAY
Check-In

During your lunch break, use this space to document your thoughts and feelings or anything that has happened at work (this can be good or bad). If you need to thoroughly document a specific incident, please complete a Personal Incident Form.

END OF THE DAY
Reflection

On a scale from 1 to 10 how was your work day?
1 being horrible and 10 being perfect

What/Who made you smile today at work?

Why did this/they make you smile?

What step(s) did you accomplish toward your professional goal today?

If you didn't work on your professional goal today, what stopped you?

How did you toot your own horn/promote yourself?

Who did you network with today? How was the experience? Was it beneficial? What will you do differently tomorrow? If you didn't network today, what stopped you?

Were there any situations that made you uncomfortable, nervous, anxious, sad, angry, cautious?

If you had a good day, describe what happened:

How can you continue to have more good days at work?

As you end your day, what three things/people are you grateful for? Why?

What are you going to do this evening to relax/practice self-care?

End Of The Day Affirmation:

DAILY DIARY
Prompt

What is something you would like to change about yourself?

PREPARING FOR
the Day

DATE

On a scale from 1 to 10 how are you feeling this morning:
1 is Horrible - Why do I even bother with this job and 10 is great - I love my job!

What action step will you work on today to help you reach your professional goal:

How will you toot your own horn/promote yourself today:

Who will you network with? Where do they work? Why are they relevant to your professional goal?

What or who might trigger or irritate you today?

What can you do to calm yourself if you become triggered/irritated?

Who will hold you accountable for your professional goal today?

TODAY'S
Affirmation

MID-DAY
Check-In

During your lunch break, use this space to document your thoughts and feelings or anything that has happened at work (this can be good or bad). If you need to thoroughly document a specific incident, please complete a Personal Incident Form.

On a scale from 1 to 10 how was your work day?
1 being horrible and 10 being perfect

What/Who made you smile today at work?

Why did this/they make you smile?

What step(s) did you accomplish toward your professional goal today?

If you didn't work on your professional goal today, what stopped you?

How did you toot your own horn/promote yourself?

Who did you network with today? How was the experience? Was it beneficial? What will you do differently tomorrow? If you didn't network today, what stopped you?

Were there any situations that made you uncomfortable, nervous, anxious, sad, angry, cautious?

If you had a good day, describe what happened:

How can you continue to have more good days at work?

As you end your day, what three things/people are you grateful for? Why?

What are you going to do this evening to relax/practice self-care?

End Of The Day Affirmation:

DAILY DIARY
Prompt

What do you need to get off your chest?

PREPARING FOR
the Day

DATE

On a scale from 1 to 10 how are you feeling this morning:
1 is Horrible - Why do I even bother with this job and 10 is great - I love my job!

What action step will you work on today to help you reach your professional goal:

How will you toot your own horn/promote yourself today:

Who will you network with? Where do they work? Why are they relevant to your professional goal?

What or who might trigger or irritate you today?

What can you do to calm yourself if you become triggered/irritated?

Who will hold you accountable for your professional goal today?

TODAY'S
Affirmation

MID-DAY
Check-In

During your lunch break, use this space to document your thoughts and feelings or anything that has happened at work (this can be good or bad). If you need to thoroughly document a specific incident, please complete a Personal Incident Form.

END OF THE DAY
Reflection

On a scale from 1 to 10 how was your work day?
1 being horrible and 10 being perfect

What/Who made you smile today at work?

Why did this/they make you smile?

What step(s) did you accomplish toward your professional goal today?

If you didn't work on your professional goal today, what stopped you?

How did you toot your own horn/promote yourself?

Who did you network with today? How was the experience? Was it beneficial? What will you do differently tomorrow? If you didn't network today, what stopped you?

Were there any situations that made you uncomfortable, nervous, anxious, sad, angry, cautious?

If you had a good day, describe what happened:

How can you continue to have more good days at work?

As you end your day, what three things/people are you grateful for? Why?

What are you going to do this evening to relax/practice self-care?

End Of The Day Affirmation:

DAILY DIARY
Prompt

What are the best ten moments of your life?

PREPARING FOR
the Day

DATE

On a scale from 1 to 10 how are you feeling this morning:
1 is Horrible - Why do I even bother with this job and 10 is great - I love my job!

What action step will you work on today to help you reach your professional goal:

How will you toot your own horn/promote yourself today:

Who will you network with? Where do they work? Why are they relevant to your professional goal?

What or who might trigger or irritate you today?

What can you do to calm yourself if you become triggered/irritated?

Who will hold you accountable for your professional goal today?

MID-DAY
Check-In

During your lunch break, use this space to document your thoughts and feelings or anything that has happened at work (this can be good or bad). If you need to thoroughly document a specific incident, please complete a Personal Incident Form.

END OF THE DAY
Reflection

On a scale from 1 to 10 how was your work day?
1 being horrible and 10 being perfect

What/Who made you smile today at work?

Why did this/they make you smile?

What step(s) did you accomplish toward your professional goal today?

If you didn't work on your professional goal today, what stopped you?

How did you toot your own horn/promote yourself?

Who did you network with today? How was the experience? Was it beneficial? What will you do differently tomorrow? If you didn't network today, what stopped you?

Were there any situations that made you uncomfortable, nervous, anxious, sad, angry, cautious?

If you had a good day, describe what happened:

How can you continue to have more good days at work?

As you end your day, what three things/people are you grateful for? Why?

What are you going to do this evening to relax/practice self-care?

End Of The Day Affirmation:

DAILY DIARY
Prompt

If you were granted three wishes, what would they be?

PREPARING FOR
the Day

DATE

On a scale from 1 to 10 how are you feeling this morning:
1 is Horrible - Why do I even bother with this job and 10 is great - I love my job!

What action step will you work on today to help you reach your professional goal:

How will you toot your own horn/promote yourself today:

Who will you network with? Where do they work? Why are they relevant to your professional goal?

What or who might trigger or irritate you today?

What can you do to calm yourself if you become triggered/irritated?

Who will hold you accountable for your professional goal today?

TODAY'S
Affirmation

MID-DAY
Check-In

During your lunch break, use this space to document your thoughts and feelings or anything that has happened at work (this can be good or bad). If you need to thoroughly document a specific incident, please complete a Personal Incident Form.

END OF THE DAY
Reflection

On a scale from 1 to 10 how was your work day?
1 being horrible and 10 being perfect

What/Who made you smile today at work?

Why did this/they make you smile?

What step(s) did you accomplish toward your professional goal today?

If you didn't work on your professional goal today, what stopped you?

How did you toot your own horn/promote yourself?

Who did you network with today? How was the experience? Was it beneficial? What will you do differently tomorrow? If you didn't network today, what stopped you?

Were there any situations that made you uncomfortable, nervous, anxious, sad, angry, cautious?

If you had a good day, describe what happened:

How can you continue to have more good days at work?

As you end your day, what three things/people are you grateful for? Why?

What are you going to do this evening to relax/practice self-care?

End Of The Day Affirmation:

DAILY DIARY
Prompt

When were you last surprised?

PREPARING FOR
the Day

DATE

On a scale from 1 to 10 how are you feeling this morning:
1 is Horrible - Why do I even bother with this job and 10 is great - I love my job!

What action step will you work on today to help you reach your professional goal:

How will you toot your own horn/promote yourself today:

Who will you network with? Where do they work? Why are they relevant to your professional goal?

What or who might trigger or irritate you today?

What can you do to calm yourself if you become triggered/irritated?

Who will hold you accountable for your professional goal today?

TODAY'S
Affirmation

MID-DAY
Check-In

During your lunch break, use this space to document your thoughts and feelings or anything that has happened at work (this can be good or bad). If you need to thoroughly document a specific incident, please complete a Personal Incident Form.

END OF THE DAY
Reflection

On a scale from 1 to 10 how was your work day?
1 being horrible and 10 being perfect

What/Who made you smile today at work?

Why did this/they make you smile?

What step(s) did you accomplish toward your professional goal today?

If you didn't work on your professional goal today, what stopped you?

How did you toot your own horn/promote yourself?

Who did you network with today? How was the experience? Was it beneficial? What will you do differently tomorrow? If you didn't network today, what stopped you?

Were there any situations that made you uncomfortable, nervous, anxious, sad, angry, cautious?

If you had a good day, describe what happened:

How can you continue to have more good days at work?

As you end your day, what three things/people are you grateful for? Why?

What are you going to do this evening to relax/practice self-care?

End Of The Day Affirmation:

DAILY DIARY
Prompt

Who is someone that inspires you and why?

PREPARING FOR
the Day

DATE

On a scale from 1 to 10 how are you feeling this morning:
1 is Horrible - Why do I even bother with this job and 10 is great - I love my job!

What action step will you work on today to help you reach your professional goal:

How will you toot your own horn/promote yourself today:

Who will you network with? Where do they work? Why are they relevant to your professional goal?

What or who might trigger or irritate you today?

What can you do to calm yourself if you become triggered/irritated?

Who will hold you accountable for your professional goal today?

TODAY'S *Affirmation*

MID-DAY
Check-In

During your lunch break, use this space to document your thoughts and feelings or anything that has happened at work (this can be good or bad). If you need to thoroughly document a specific incident, please complete a Personal Incident Form.

END OF THE DAY
Reflection

On a scale from 1 to 10 how was your work day?
1 being horrible and 10 being perfect

What/Who made you smile today at work?

Why did this/they make you smile?

What step(s) did you accomplish toward your professional goal today?

If you didn't work on your professional goal today, what stopped you?

How did you toot your own horn/promote yourself?

Who did you network with today? How was the experience? Was it beneficial? What will you do differently tomorrow? If you didn't network today, what stopped you?

Were there any situations that made you uncomfortable, nervous, anxious, sad, angry, cautious?

If you had a good day, describe what happened:

How can you continue to have more good days at work?

As you end your day, what three things/people are you grateful for? Why?

What are you going to do this evening to relax/practice self-care?

End Of The Day Affirmation:

DAILY DIARY
Prompt

What do you need to get off your chest?

PREPARING FOR *the Day*

DATE

On a scale from 1 to 10 how are you feeling this morning:
1 is Horrible - Why do I even bother with this job and 10 is great - I love my job!

What action step will you work on today to help you reach your professional goal:

How will you toot your own horn/promote yourself today:

Who will you network with? Where do they work? Why are they relevant to your professional goal?

What or who might trigger or irritate you today?

What can you do to calm yourself if you become triggered/irritated?

Who will hold you accountable for your professional goal today?

TODAY'S *Affirmation*

MID-DAY
Check-In

During your lunch break, use this space to document your thoughts and feelings or anything that has happened at work (this can be good or bad). If you need to thoroughly document a specific incident, please complete a Personal Incident Form.

END OF THE DAY
Reflection

On a scale from 1 to 10 how was your work day?
1 being horrible and 10 being perfect

What/Who made you smile today at work?

Why did this/they make you smile?

What step(s) did you accomplish toward your professional goal today?

If you didn't work on your professional goal today, what stopped you?

How did you toot your own horn/promote yourself?

Who did you network with today? How was the experience? Was it beneficial? What will you do differently tomorrow? If you didn't network today, what stopped you?

Were there any situations that made you uncomfortable, nervous, anxious, sad, angry, cautious?

If you had a good day, describe what happened:

How can you continue to have more good days at work?

As you end your day, what three things/people are you grateful for? Why?

What are you going to do this evening to relax/practice self-care?

End Of The Day Affirmation:

DAILY DIARY
Prompt

If you could travel back in time, where would you go and why?

PREPARING FOR
the Day

DATE

On a scale from 1 to 10 how are you feeling this morning:
1 is Horrible - Why do I even bother with this job and 10 is great - I love my job!

What action step will you work on today to help you reach your professional goal:

How will you toot your own horn/promote yourself today:

Who will you network with? Where do they work? Why are they relevant to your professional goal?

What or who might trigger or irritate you today?

What can you do to calm yourself if you become triggered/irritated?

Who will hold you accountable for your professional goal today?

TODAY'S *Affirmation*

MID-DAY
Check-In

During your lunch break, use this space to document your thoughts and feelings or anything that has happened at work (this can be good or bad). If you need to thoroughly document a specific incident, please complete a Personal Incident Form.

END OF THE DAY
Reflection

On a scale from 1 to 10 how was your work day?
1 being horrible and 10 being perfect

What/Who made you smile today at work?

Why did this/they make you smile?

What step(s) did you accomplish toward your professional goal today?

If you didn't work on your professional goal today, what stopped you?

How did you toot your own horn/promote yourself?

Who did you network with today? How was the experience? Was it beneficial? What will you do differently tomorrow? If you didn't network today, what stopped you?

Were there any situations that made you uncomfortable, nervous, anxious, sad, angry, cautious?

If you had a good day, describe what happened:

How can you continue to have more good days at work?

As you end your day, what three things/people are you grateful for? Why?

What are you going to do this evening to relax/practice self-care?

End Of The Day Affirmation:

DAILY DIARY
Prompt

Describe your dream vacation.

PREPARING FOR
the Day

DATE

On a scale from 1 to 10 how are you feeling this morning:
1 is Horrible - Why do I even bother with this job and 10 is great - I love my job!

What action step will you work on today to help you reach your professional goal:

How will you toot your own horn/promote yourself today:

Who will you network with? Where do they work? Why are they relevant to your professional goal?

What or who might trigger or irritate you today?

What can you do to calm yourself if you become triggered/irritated?

Who will hold you accountable for your professional goal today?

MID-DAY
Check-In

During your lunch break, use this space to document your thoughts and feelings or anything that has happened at work (this can be good or bad). If you need to thoroughly document a specific incident, please complete a Personal Incident Form.

END OF THE DAY
Reflection

On a scale from 1 to 10 how was your work day?
1 being horrible and 10 being perfect

What/Who made you smile today at work?

Why did this/they make you smile?

What step(s) did you accomplish toward your professional goal today?

If you didn't work on your professional goal today, what stopped you?

How did you toot your own horn/promote yourself?

Who did you network with today? How was the experience? Was it beneficial? What will you do differently tomorrow? If you didn't network today, what stopped you?

Were there any situations that made you uncomfortable, nervous, anxious, sad, angry, cautious?

If you had a good day, describe what happened:

How can you continue to have more good days at work?

As you end your day, what three things/people are you grateful for? Why?

What are you going to do this evening to relax/practice self-care?

End Of The Day Affirmation:

DAILY DIARY
Prompt

What things change your mood from positive to negative?

PREPARING FOR
the Day

DATE

On a scale from 1 to 10 how are you feeling this morning:
1 is Horrible - Why do I even bother with this job and 10 is great - I love my job!

What action step will you work on today to help you reach your professional goal:

How will you toot your own horn/promote yourself today:

Who will you network with? Where do they work? Why are they relevant to your professional goal?

What or who might trigger or irritate you today?

What can you do to calm yourself if you become triggered/irritated?

Who will hold you accountable for your professional goal today?

TODAY'S
Affirmation

MID-DAY
Check-In

During your lunch break, use this space to document your thoughts and feelings or anything that has happened at work (this can be good or bad). If you need to thoroughly document a specific incident, please complete a Personal Incident Form.

END OF THE DAY
Reflection

On a scale from 1 to 10 how was your work day?
1 being horrible and 10 being perfect

What/Who made you smile today at work?

Why did this/they make you smile?

What step(s) did you accomplish toward your professional goal today?

If you didn't work on your professional goal today, what stopped you?

How did you toot your own horn/promote yourself?

Who did you network with today? How was the experience? Was it beneficial? What will you do differently tomorrow? If you didn't network today, what stopped you?

Were there any situations that made you uncomfortable, nervous, anxious, sad, angry, cautious?

If you had a good day, describe what happened:

How can you continue to have more good days at work?

As you end your day, what three things/people are you grateful for? Why?

What are you going to do this evening to relax/practice self-care?

End Of The Day Affirmation:

DAILY DIARY
Prompt

What is an amazing memory you would like to create?

PREPARING FOR
the Day

DATE

On a scale from 1 to 10 how are you feeling this morning:
1 is Horrible - Why do I even bother with this job and 10 is great - I love my job!

What action step will you work on today to help you reach your professional goal:

How will you toot your own horn/promote yourself today:

Who will you network with? Where do they work? Why are they relevant to your professional goal?

What or who might trigger or irritate you today?

What can you do to calm yourself if you become triggered/irritated?

Who will hold you accountable for your professional goal today?

TODAY'S *Affirmation*

MID-DAY
Check-In

During your lunch break, use this space to document your thoughts and feelings or anything that has happened at work (this can be good or bad). If you need to thoroughly document a specific incident, please complete a Personal Incident Form.

END OF THE DAY
Reflection

On a scale from 1 to 10 how was your work day?
1 being horrible and 10 being perfect

What/Who made you smile today at work?

Why did this/they make you smile?

What step(s) did you accomplish toward your professional goal today?

If you didn't work on your professional goal today, what stopped you?

How did you toot your own horn/promote yourself?

Who did you network with today? How was the experience? Was it beneficial? What will you do differently tomorrow? If you didn't network today, what stopped you?

Were there any situations that made you uncomfortable, nervous, anxious, sad, angry, cautious?

If you had a good day, describe what happened:

How can you continue to have more good days at work?

As you end your day, what three things/people are you grateful for? Why?

What are you going to do this evening to relax/practice self-care?

End Of The Day Affirmation:

DAILY DIARY
Prompt

Describe your dream job.

PREPARING FOR
the Day

DATE

On a scale from 1 to 10 how are you feeling this morning:
1 is Horrible - Why do I even bother with this job and 10 is great - I love my job!

What action step will you work on today to help you reach your professional goal:

How will you toot your own horn/promote yourself today:

Who will you network with? Where do they work? Why are they relevant to your professional goal?

What or who might trigger or irritate you today?

What can you do to calm yourself if you become triggered/irritated?

Who will hold you accountable for your professional goal today?

TODAY'S Affirmation

MID-DAY
Check-In

During your lunch break, use this space to document your thoughts and feelings or anything that has happened at work (this can be good or bad). If you need to thoroughly document a specific incident, please complete a Personal Incident Form.

END OF THE DAY
Reflection

On a scale from 1 to 10 how was your work day?
1 being horrible and 10 being perfect

What/Who made you smile today at work?

Why did this/they make you smile?

What step(s) did you accomplish toward your professional goal today?

If you didn't work on your professional goal today, what stopped you?

How did you toot your own horn/promote yourself?

Who did you network with today? How was the experience? Was it beneficial? What will you do differently tomorrow? If you didn't network today, what stopped you?

Were there any situations that made you uncomfortable, nervous, anxious, sad, angry, cautious?

If you had a good day, describe what happened:

How can you continue to have more good days at work?

As you end your day, what three things/people are you grateful for? Why?

What are you going to do this evening to relax/practice self-care?

End Of The Day Affirmation:

DAILY DIARY
Prompt

How are you feeling after completing this workbook
and one month of documenting your work days?

CONCLUSION

The goal of this workbook and work diary was to change the narrative for Black women when it comes to healing. I wanted to create a resource that would help us to understand that unlike white women, we have multiple demons that we are fighting on a daily basis. We have learned to create a multi-layered emotional armor to deal with systemic racism, family issues, and toxic workplaces. I want Black women to realize that we don't have to continue to wear these different layers of emotional protective gear and that it is okay to remove the armor. I want us to understand that we can heal, and it doesn't have to be at the hands of old white men and privilege suburban white women who don't understand our struggle and leave us feeling more confused than when we first started our healing journey.

Society has convinced us not to stop and reflect on how we have adapted to a life filled with trauma and oppression or the mental gymnastics required to accomplish such a feat. This workbook was created to challenge all of that and show you how to start the healing process through the lens of a Black woman.

Dr. Carey Yazeed

ABOUT THE
Author

Dr. Carey Yazeed is a qualitative researcher and the bestselling author of Shut'em Down: Black Women, Racism and Corporate America and How Toxic Workspaces Impact Black Women. She uses her platform to collect and share the untold stories of Black women. She is a graduate of Louisiana State University with a Ph.D. in Higher Education Leadership and Research, Tulane University with a Master in Social Work and Southern University A&M College with a Bachelor of Science in Liberal Arts (Psychology). She resides in South Louisiana and is a member of Delta Sigma Theta Sorority, Inc. To learn more about Dr. Yazeed visit www.drcareyyazeed.com